EXPERIMENTS
IN THE MECHANICS OF
HUMAN MOVEMENT

H. Joseph Scheuchenzuber
Associate Professor
Springfield College
Springfield, MA
1983

Mouvement Publications
109 E. State St.
Ithaca, N.Y. 14850

Woodstock
19 Oaks Way, Gayton
Heswall, Wirral
L60 3SP England

Woorkarrim
Lot #7, Strathmore Drive
Torquay 3228 Australia

Copyright © 1983 by Mouvement Publications.
Layout by: Sandy Sharpe
Typeset by: Strehle's Computerized Typesetting, Ithaca, New York
Printed in the United States of America
by McNaughton Gunn, Ann Arbor, Michigan

ISBN 0932392-12-1

PREFACE

This manual has evolved from laboratory experiences conducted over an 8 year period. The information presented is general in overall direction containing portions which deal with both the kinesiological and the biomechanical aspects of the study of human movement, it is not directly associated with any current text.

The conduct of most of the laboratory sessions require commonly available or homemade inexpensive equipment. The procedures, in most cases, do not specify specific equipment or directions which require use of particular items, this allows the laboratory instructor to verbally modify the procedures to meet with the limitations of his/her laboratory facility. Through Mouvement Publications, the author plans to make available the following items as an instructors packet: (1) a set of suggested instructions for the construction of simple needed equipment, (2) computer program listings for student use in computation and verification of laboratory results and (3) sequential slide sets representing various human motions (used in Quantitative Motion Analysis Lab).

The experiences were designed so that the students would be active during the conduct of many of the sessions. This philosophy dealing with student activity has been positively reacted to by students and appears to be a great factor in their learning and retention of the material presented.

General Preparations for Laboratory Experiences

1. Prepare yourself for your laboratory activities by reading the purpose, theory and procedures for the assigned laboratory experience prior to your arrival at the laboratory.

2. Record the required information completely and accurately during the laboratory period.

3. Complete the required submission forms as soon after the laboratory session as possible.

4. Be prepared to submit the required submission forms at the beginning of the next laboratory session.
   (NOTE: submit only the required submission forms attached together with a staple or paper clip. DO NOT fold the corners and expect this procedure to hold them together. Also, DO NOT submit the entire laboratory experience description.)

TABLE OF CONTENTS

INTRODUCTION

PURPOSE

To complete some laboratory submission forms which you will be using at the end of the next three laboratory sessions to determine if your own personal biases are correctly founded.

To become familiar with the concepts of relationships and how these may be used to evaluate or predict performances.

THEORY

Anthropometry (the measurement of the human organism) and its relationship to performance has been a question posed by coaches and researchers for many years. The biases imposed by coaches in team selection is a predominant example of a search for the superior performer. These biases range from purely subjective selection of basketball players, because they are tall, to more scientifically supported selection of track sprinters based on selected limb lengths or ranges of motion. It is commonly assumed that some relationship exists between anthropometric measurements (be they lengths, volumes, or ranges) and selected performances, and it is the purpose of the first three laboratory experiences in this manual to determine if, for your laboratory group, these relationships exist.

In order to make an objective evaluation of these relationships it will be necessary to complete four (4) separate portions of this experiment. The first of these portions will ask you to subjectively impose your biases in the determination of relationships between various measurable factors from the body and selected measurable performance variables. In this section you will be asked to indicate your feelings as to what relationships will exist between described variables and give a brief but logical reason why you would expect such a relationship.

The procedures which follow will be explained in more detail by your laboratory instructor during your first laboratory meeting and will be completed by you outside the laboratory setting and prior to your second laboratory session.

PROCEDURES

1. Prior to your next laboratory meeting during which you will begin to take the needed measurements for relationship evaluation, you will complete the attached submission forms.

2. The completion of the submission forms will require that you make subjective evaluations of the relationships you think will exist between variables which you will then measure during your next three sessions.

3. The evaluations which are requested ask you to choose among the following: 1. positively related, 2. not related, and 3. negatively related.
    NOTE: As an explanation of these relationships:

    1. Positive Relationship — A positive relationship exists between two variables when as one variable increases in value while the other variable also increases in value.
    2. No Relationship — No relationship exists between two variables when: (a) as one variable increases in value the other remains unchanged, or (b) as one value increases in value the other increases or decreases unpredictability.
    3. Negative Relationship — A negative relationship exists between two variables when as one variable increases in value the other variable decreases in value.

A more thorough explanation of these relationships and a description of the variables to be measured and considered will be available from your laboratory instructor during your first laboratory session.

SUBMISSION FORMS — Introduction

Name _____ Section _____

Performance Variables	Anthropometric Variables	Negative −1	Relationship None 0	Positive +1
1. Hip Hyperextension Strength	Thigh circumference		│	
	Lower Leg volume		│	
	Leg length		│	
	Stature height		│	
	Total Body weight		│	
	Hip ROM hyperextension		│	

Explanation of your biases. Why? _____

_____

_____

Performance Variables	Anthropometric Variables	Negative −1	Relationship None 0	Positive +1
2. Elbow Flexion Strength	Upper Arm circumference		│	
	Lower Arm volume		│	
	Shoulder diameter		│	
	Stature height		│	
	Total Body weight		│	
	Wrist ROM flexion		│	

Explanation of your biases. Why? _____

_____

_____

		Relationship	
Performance Variables	Anthropometric Variables	Negative −1	None 0	Positive +1

3. Agility

	Negative −1	None 0	Positive +1
Thigh circumference				
Leg and Foot volume				
Hip diameter				
Stature height				
Total Body weight				
Knee ROM flexion				

Explanation of your biases. Why? _____

_____

_____

_____

4. Starting
   Speed
   (10 meters)

	Negative −1	None 0	Positive +1
Thigh circumference			
Leg and Foot volume			
Hip diameter			
Stature height			
Total Body weight			
Ankle ROM flexion			

Explanation of your biases. Why? _____

_____

_____

_____

4

Performance Variables	Anthropometric Variables	Negative −1	Relationship None 0	Positive +1
5. Running Speed (30 meters)	Thigh circumference			
	Leg and Foot volume			
	Hip diameter			
	Stature height			
	Total Body weight			
	Hip ROM hyperextension			

Explanation of your biases. Why? _____

_____

_____

_____

Performance Variables	Anthropometric Variables	Negative −1	Relationship None 0	Positive +1
6. Muscular Endurance (bent arm hang)	Upper Arm circumference			
	Arm and Hand volume			
	Shoulder diameter			
	Stature height			
	Total Body weight			
	Elbow ROM flexion			

Explanation of your biases. Why? _____

_____

_____

_____

Performance Variables	Anthropometric Variables	Negative −1	Relationship None 0	Positive +1
7. Power (vertical jump test)				
	Thigh circumference			
	Leg and Foot volume			
	Hip diameter			
	Leg length			
	Total Body weight			
	Knee ROM flexion			

Explanation of your biases. Why? _____

_____

_____

_____

GONIOMETRY
range of motion

PURPOSE

To determine the active and passive ranges of motion for selected body joints by means of orthopedic goniometry.

THEORY

In order to understand better the nature of human motion, it is of value to establish the normal limits within which that motion will exist. In most cases, the general or total motion man accomplishes in performing his many, varied activities is the sum of a combination of partial motions. These motions involve the rotations of limbs or limb segments about an axis. A knowledge of the range of motion of a segment about a joint axis lays the foundation for further study of man's total motion within his environment.

Normal range of motion at a particular joint will exist within certain limitations, as presented in population norms, and will depend upon a variety of factors. Serious departures from these normal limits or discrepancies between measurements at a particular joint and its contralateral equivalent may display atypical situations. Similarly, forces which cause segments to rotate beyond their normal limits may inflict injury upon the joint.

Primary factors which determine the range of motion at a joint:
1. The shape of the articular surfaces (type of joint)
2. The articular ligaments (their length and positioning)
3. The locations and dynamics of muscles and tendons which influence the joint

In addition, body somatotype may further influence range of motion if extreme endomorphy or mesomorphy exist.

Total range of motion is commonly delineated into two aspects. These are the active range of motion and the passive range of motion. Both ranges are measured in angular degrees as the limb segment rotates transcribing an arc about a particular joint axis. Active range of motion is that portion of the total range of motion in which the subject is capable of moving a segment by voluntary muscular contraction. Passive range of motion exceeds the limits of active motion when an external force is applied and causes further rotation of the body segment. The passive measurements, then, should always present a larger range of motion than those measurements taken actively.

The quantity of difference between these two aspects of the range of motion, active and passive, is primarily a result of individual muscle tone. As muscle tone decreases, active range of motion normally decreases. If ligamental structure and the distensibility properties of the antagonistic muscles remain unaltered, passive range of motion will not be affected.

EQUIPMENT

Skin marking pencils
Rulers or straight edges
Goniometers

REFERENCES

American Academy of Orthopedic Surgeons. **Joint Motion: Method of Measuring and Recording.** 1965.

Cave, E. F. and Roberts, S. M. "A Method of Measuring and Recording Joint Function," **Journal of Bone and Joint Surgery.** 18:2:455-466, April, 1936.

Wells, K. F. and Luttgens, K. **Kinesiology: Scientific Basis of Human Motion.** 6th edition, Philadelphia: W. B. Saunders Company, 1976.

PROCEDURES

1. Locate the required bony landmarks through the process of palpation and place a small mark on these points with the skin marker provided.

   Landmarks to be located:
   a. Greater tubercle of the humerus (approximately 5cm below the acromion process of the scapula)
   b. Head of the radius
   c. Styloid process of the ulna
   d. Head of the fifth metacarpal
   e. Greater trochanter of the femur
   f. Lateral condyle of the femur
   g. Lateral malleolus
   h. Proximal end of the fifth metatarsal

2. Draw a light line on the limb connecting adjacent landmarks to define the mechanical axis for each segment.

3. Have the subject to be measured assume the "Base Starting Position" for each joint as described on the submission forms.

4. Place the goniometer on the joint to be measured according to the following criteria:
   a. The axis of the goniometer is placed on the joint axis for the particular movement being measured.
   b. The stationary arm of the goniometer is placed along the mechanical axis of the proximal segment.
   c. The movable arm of the goniometer is placed along the mechanical axis of the distal segment.

5. On the submission form provided, record the goniometric measure of the Base Starting Position for each of the joints to be evaluated.

6. In the appropriate space on each of the submission forms record the goniometric readings for the following four positions:
   a. Maximum active joint flexion
   b. Maximum passive joint flexion
   c. Maximum active joint hyperextension
   d. Maximum passive joint hyperextension (NOTE: use only moderate force in establishing passive hyperextensions of the elbow and knee joints.)

7. Determine the range of motion in each direction (flexion, hyperextension) and under each condition (active, passive) by calculating the absolute value of the difference between your Base Starting Position and each active and passive reading. Present your results in the spaces provided on the submission forms.

8. Graph your results on the graph paper provided and as illustrated by the example.

9. Compare your results to the average range of motion measures provided below. If substantial differences exist, speculate on the reasons for those differences in the space provided.

AVERAGE ACTIVE RANGES OF MOTION

Joint	Flexion (degrees)	Hyperextension (degrees)
Elbow	146	0
Wrist	73	70
Hip	113	28
Knee	134	10
Ankle	48	18

SUBMISSION FORMS — Goniometry

NAME _____ SECTION_____

RANGES OF MOTION — degrees

	FLEXION		HYPEREXTENSION	
	Active	Passive	Active	Passive
ELBOW				
WRIST				
HIP				
KNEE				
ANKLE				

Where did you find differences between your ranges of motion and those presented as the average? (Be specific as to joint and difference found.)

_____

_____

_____

_____

_____

_____

_____

_____

_____

_____

_____

Speculate on possible reasons for the differences you have found.

_____

_____

_____

_____

_____

_____

_____

_____

_____

_____

ELBOW

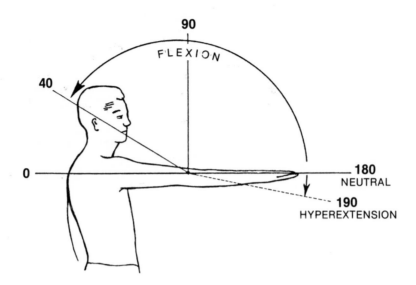

(Figure modified from AAOS **Joint Motion: Method of Measuring and Recording.** 1965)

Base Starting Position: From anatomical position, shoulder flexion to 90 degrees with elbow at 180 degrees (NOTE: lower arm should remain in pronation.)

Goniometer Placement:
a. Proximal point of proximal segment — Greater tubercle of the humerus
b. Approximate joint axis — Head of the radius
c. Distal point of distal segment — Styloid process of ulna

Measurements:		Ranges of Motion (degrees)
Base Starting Position _____ degrees		
Max. Active Flexion _____ degrees		_____
Max. Passive Flexion _____ degrees		_____
Max. Active Hyperextension _____ degrees		_____
Max. Passive Hyperextension _____ degrees		_____

WRIST

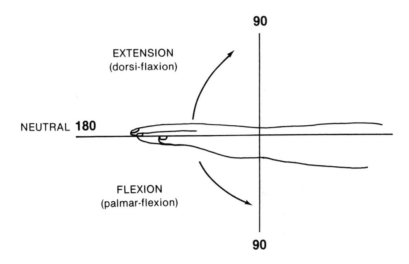

(Figure modified from AAOS **Joint Motion: Method of Measuring and Recording.** 1965)

Base Starting Position: Shoulder flexion to 90 degrees, lower arm in pronation, elbow and wrist at 180 degrees

Goniometer Placement:
a. Proximal point of proximal segment — Head of the radius
b. Approximate joint axis — Styloid process of the ulna
c. Distal point of the distal segment — Head of the fifth metacarpal

Measurements:

		Ranges of Motion (degrees)
Base Starting Position	_____ degrees	
Max. Active Flexion	_____ degrees	_____
Max. Passive Flexion	_____ degrees	_____
Max. Active Hyperextension	_____ degrees	_____
Max. Passive Hyperextension	_____ degrees	_____

HIP (FLEXION)

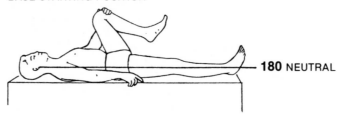

BASE STARTING POSITION

180 NEUTRAL

(Figure modified from AAOS **Joint Motion: Method of Measuring and Recording.** 1965)

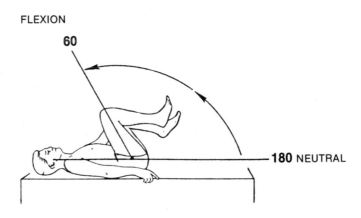

FLEXION

60

180 NEUTRAL

Base Starting Position: Subject lies supine upon a firm, flat surface with the opposite hip held in full flexion. This position flattens the lumbar spine.

Goniometer Placement:
a. Proximal point of proximal segment — Glenoid humeral joint
b. Approximate joint axis — Greater trochanter of femur
c. Distal point of distal segment — Lateral condyle of femur

Measurements:

Base Starting Position _____ degrees

Max. Active Flexion _____ degrees

Max. Passive Flexion _____ degrees

Ranges of
Motion
(degrees)

_____

_____

HIP (HYPEREXTENSION)

BASE STARTING POSITION

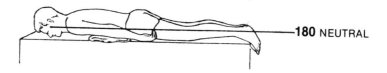

(Figure modified from AAOS **Joint Motion: Method of Measuring and Recording.** 1965)

EXTENSION

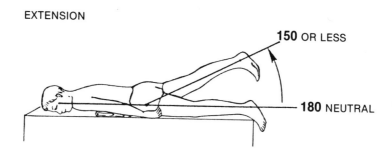

Base Starting Position: Subject lies prone on a firm, flat surface

Goniometer Placement:
a. Proximal point of proximal segment — Glenoid humeral joint
b. Approximat joint axis — Greater trochanter of femur
c. Distal point of distal segment — Lateral condyle of femur

Measurements:

Ranges of Motion (degrees)

Base Starting Position _____ degrees

Max. Active Hyperextension _____ degrees   _____

Max. Passive Hyperextension _____ degrees   _____

15

KNEE

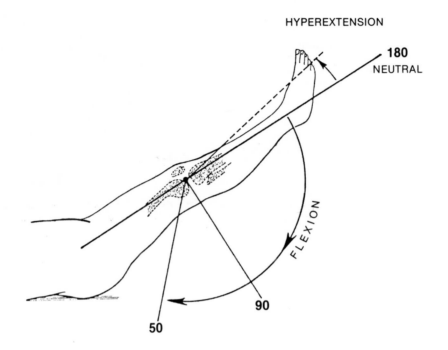

HYPEREXTENSION

180
NEUTRAL

FLEXION

90

50

(Figure modified from AAOS **Joint Motion: Method of Measuring and Recording.** 1965)

Base Starting Position: Subject in a supine position with the knee at 180 degrees

Goniometer Placement:
a. Proximal point of proximal segment — Greater trochanter of the femur
b. Approximate joint axis — Lateral condyle of the femur
c. Distal point of distal segment — Lateral malleolus

Measurements:

Ranges of
Motion
(degrees)

Base Starting Position _____ degrees

Max. Active Flexion _____ degrees   _____

Max. Passive Flexion _____ degrees   _____

Max. Active Hyperextension _____ degrees   _____

Max. Passive Hyperextension _____ degrees   _____

ANKLE

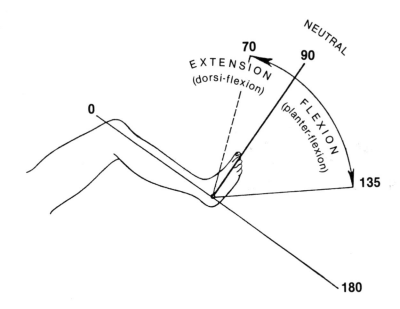

(Figure modified from AAOS **Joint Motion: Method of Measuring and Recording.** 1965)

Base Starting Position: The leg at 90 degrees to the thigh and the foot at 90 degrees to the leg

Goniometer Placement:
a. Proximal point of proximal segment — Lateral condyle of femur
b. Approximate joint axis — Lateral malleolus
c. Distal point of distal segment — Proximal end of the fifth metatarsal

Measurements:		Ranges of Motion (degrees)
Base Starting Position	_____ degrees	
Max. Active Flexion	_____ degrees	_____
Max. Passive Flexion	_____ degrees	_____
Max. Active Hyperextension	_____ degrees	_____
Max. Passive Hyperextension	_____ degrees	_____

The following is a Bar Graph of the Goniometric Evaluation of Active and Passive Ranges of Motion of Selected Joints

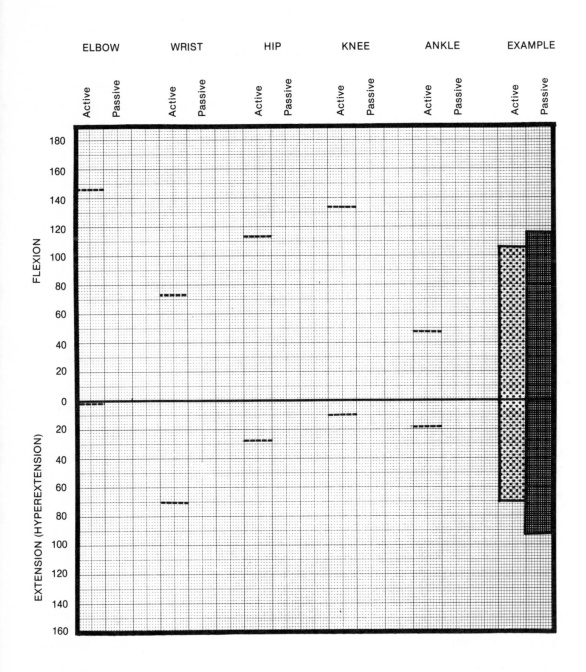

How does the palpation of the landmarks influence the measurement of the ranges of motion? _____

_____

_____

_____

_____

Explain the three factors which appear to restrict range of motion. _____

_____

_____

_____

_____

_____

_____

_____

_____

_____

_____

_____

_____

Select one joint from those presented on your graph. Calculate and present the total active range of motion for that joint (maximum active flexion to maximum active hyperextension) and describe movements which normally require the entire range. _____

_____

_____

_____

_____

_____

_____

_____

_____

_____

_____

_____

_____

ANTHROPOMETRY

PURPOSE

To provide quantifiable anthropometric measures other than goniometric angular measures to be used for determination of relationships with measures of selected performances.

To provide exposure to various measurement techniques used in anthropometry including segmental: circumferences, diameters, lengths, volumes and weights.

THEORY

The area which is concerned with the measurement of the physical characteristics of the body is termed anthropometrics. Many researchers in the fields of physical education and human factors engineering spend great amounts of time accumulating information dealing with the size of the human body parts. The need for the accumulation of this information becomes apparent when an individual is in the process of obtaining an object which was designed for human use. An automobile in which the driver can not reach the steering wheel or brake pedal is of little use. Sports implements which are too long or short serve little or no purpose to the athlete. Even clothing from the rack with disproportionately long sleeves would not be desirable. It is therefore obvious that body or body component size is very important.

In physical education, it has been suggested that particular individuals will excell in an athletic endeavor because of their body size. Basketball is a prime example of such an activity. Coaches of other sports seek performers with extraordinary limb lengths, large or small muscle girths or lesser amounts of adipose tissue.

The biases applied by coaches have been passed from teacher to pupil over generations; some are well founded, others are completely without basis. It is therefore assumed that if physical educators are capable of making measurements and determining relationships among physical traits and performance values, that biases used in athlete selection will be defendable. With this in mind, this laboratory experience was designed to provide future physical educators exposure to anthropometric measurement techniques.

EQUIPMENT

Tape measures
Metric scales
Submersion tanks
Anthropometric calipers
Anthopometers

REFERENCES

Luttgens, K. and Wells, K.F. **Kinesiology.** Philadelphia: Saunders College Publishing, 1982.

U.S. Consumer Product Safety Commission, **Anthropometry of Infants, Children, and Youths to Age 18 for Product Safety Design.** U.S. Government Publishing Office, 1977.

PROCEDURES (General)

1. Every member of the laboratory group will be measured in each of the anthropometric variables required.

2. Each member of the laboratory group will be assigned to a measurement group and will provide that measurement to all the other members of their laboratory group. The procedures for all necessary anthropometric measures follow. Be as accurate as possible in your measurements and follow the procedures exactly as described.

3. Perform each measurement 3 times, record the measurement in the appropriate space on the recording form, compute the mean of the three performances and record it in the space provided on your recording forms.

PROCEDURES (Circumferences)

1. All circumferences should be measured in a horizontal plane.

2. The measuring tape should be placed at the appropriate anatomical location and pulled taut so that the tape follows the skin's contour. The tape should not be so taut as to depress the skin's surface.

   a. Thigh Circumference — the subject should stand erect with the legs slightly separated, weight evenly distributed. With the provided tape, measure the horizontal circumference of the right thigh at the level of the gluteal furrow.

   b. Upper Arm Circumference — the subject should stand erect with arms hanging at their sides. With the provided tape, measure the horizontal circumference of the right are midway between the shoulder and the elbow.

PROCEDURES (Volumes)

1. All volumes are measured by the water displacement method. The submersion tank is filled until at the level of the overflow. The selected segment is slowly submerged until the selected anatomical landmark is reached. The collected water from the overflow is measured for volume and this value is recorded as the limb volume.

   a. Leg and Foot Volume — A horizontal circle should be drawn connecting the medial and lateral condyles of the femur of the dominant leg. The foot and leg segments should be submerged slowly until the surface of the submersion tank is at the circle level. The volume of the collected water is measured and the results recorded.

   b. Lower Arm and Hand Volume — A horizontal circle should be drawn connecting the lateral and medial epicondyles of the humerus of the dominant arm. The hand

and arm segments should be submerged slowly until the surface of the submersion tank is at the circle level. The volume of the collected water is measured and the results recorded.

PROCEDURES (Diameters)

1. All diameters should be measured along a transverse axis between the points described.

2. The calipers should be held horizontal with their interior surfaces touching the required anatomical landmarks.

   a. Biacromial Diameter — The subject should stand erect with the arms hanging at the sides. The internal edges of the blades of the calipers should be placed on the right and left acromion processes and the horizontal distance between these is the biacromial diameter which is to be recorded.

   b. Hip Diameter at Trocanters — The subject should stand erect with feet together, weight evenly distributed. The internal edges of the blades of the calipers should be placed against the skin at the height of the greater trocanters. The horizontal reading from the caliper's scale is the hip diameter which should be recorded.

PROCEDURES (Heights)

1. All heights should be measured along the longitudinal axis for the segment or total body (no shoes or socks).

2. The anthropometers should be moved to the selected anatomical location and placed as not to move the body tissues which are touched.

   a. Trochanteric Height — The subject should stand erect with the feet together, weight evenly distributed. The pointed blade of the anthropometer should run horizontal from the scale to the location of the right greater trocanter. The vertical distance from the standing surface to the right greater trochanter should be read and recorded as this measure.

   b. Total Body or Stature Height — The subject should stand erect with the head position defined by the lower orbit edge of the right eye and hole of the right ear in horizontal alignment. The flat surface of the anthropometer's blade should run horizontally from the scale to the skull's vertex. The vertical distance between the vertex of the skull and the standing surface should be read and recorded as this measure.

PROCEDURE (Weight)

1. Total Body Weight — The subject should stand on a metric clinical scale dressed in shorts and short sleeve shirt (no shoes or socks). The weight is measured by the evaluator and is recorded to the nearest .1 of a kilogram.

SUBMISSION FORMS — Anthropometry

Name _____ Section _____

Recordings of Anthropometric Measures

Circumferences

Thigh

reading 1 _____ cms.

reading 2 _____ cms.

reading 3 _____ cms.   Mean _____ cms.

Upper arm

reading 1 _____ cms.

reading 2 _____ cms.

reading 3 _____ cms.   Mean _____ cms.

Volumes

Leg and foot

reading 1 _____ mls.

reading 2 - _____ mls.

reading 3 _____ mls.   Mean _____ mls.

Lower arm and hand

reading 1 _____ mls.

reading 2 _____ mls.

reading 3 _____ mls.   Mean _____ mls.

Diameters

Biacromial

reading 1 - _____ cms.

reading 2 _____ cms.

reading 3 - _____ cms.   Mean _____ cms.

Hip at trocanters

reading 1 - _____ cms.

reading 2 _____ cms.

reading 3 _____ cms.   Mean _____ cms.

Heights

Trochanteric

reading 1 _____ cms.

reading 2 - _____ cms.

reading 3 - _____ cms.   Mean _____ cms.

Stature

    reading 1 _____ cms.

    reading 2 _____ cms.

    reading 3 _____ cms.   Mean _____ cms.

Weight

  Total body

    reading 1 _____ kgs.

    reading 2 _____ kgs.

    reading 3 _____ kgs.   Mean _____ kgs.

QUESTIONS

As a future coach, what value is there to knowing relative anthropometric measures of possible performers for your team. (Select 2 of those which you have conducted during this laboratory experience.)

measure _____

value _____

_____

_____

_____

_____

measure _____

value _____

_____

_____

_____

_____

In the evaluation of a person's general fitness, what anthropometric measurements would you conduct? Why?

_____

_____

_____

_____

_____

_____

In conducting or observing the anthropometric measurement procedures during your laboratory experience, where did you notice inaccuracies occurring? Why?

_____

_____

_____

_____

_____

_____

PERFORMANCE
EVALUATION

PURPOSE

To provide quantifiable measures of selected performances to allow for determination of relationships with selected anthropometric and goniometric measures.

To provide exposure to measurement of selected tests including: strength, speed, power, agility and muscular endurance.

THEORY

All athletic performances are combinations of a relatively few physical traits. The ability to perform some combination of these traits is the basis for success in sport. In some activities, time and/or distance determine success, others require brute strength while yet others require the ability to produce traits in a selected sequence. If a coach or physical educator is able to determine the specific traits required for the skill being learned, and then accurately measure the performance of those traits, he/she should have the ability to predict those persons who will be able to perform at a high level. The selection and application of commonly acceptable tests for various physical performances is normally included in courses which fall under the category of "Performance Assessment". Hence, the exposure attempted within the context of this laboratory experience will be superficial in nature.

The tests selected for evaluation at this time are not assumed to be the most efficient for testing the traits we are concerned with, but are relatively easy to conduct and cover a wide range of desirable components in athletic performance.

The test items to be considered in this laboratory experience can be grouped into the following categories: (1) STRENGTH - isometric hip hyperextension and isometric elbow flexion, (2) SPEED - 10 yard dash and 40 yard dash (3) POWER - standing vertical jump, (4) AGILITY - timed multidirectional agility test and (5) MUSCULAR ENDURANCE - timed bent arm hang.

EQUIPMENT

Cable Tensiometers
Vertical Jump

Stop Watches
Tape Measure

DEFINITIONS

Strength - The ability of the body to exert force on the external environment through the generation of muscular tension and the application of the body's lever system.

Speed - Rate of performance.

Power - The rate of the performance of mechanical work.

Agility - The ability to change directions rapidly and accurately.

Endurance -The ability for a muscle to sustain the application of force.

PROCEDURES (General)

1. Every member of the laboratory group will perform each of the trait tests required.

2. Each member of the laboratory group will be an administrator for each test. The procedures for administration of each test follow. Be as accurate as possible in your measurements and follow the procedures exactly as listed.

PROCEDURES (Strength Tests)

1. Position the subject on the strength measurement boards as described by your laboratory instructor for either the hip hyperextension or elbow flexion test.

2. Be sure that the cable on which the tensiometer is to be placed is perpendicular to the limb creating the torque.

3. Measure accurately the distance from the joint which is active to the placement of the limb retaining strap. Record this measurement on the subject's recording form.

4. Allow the subject to complete 3 maximal muscular contractions (using the described movements) and record the tensiometer measures in the appropriate location after each contraction. (NOTES - contractions should be slow and controlled against a taut tensiometer cable with no initial jerk on the limb retaining strap and the total leg segment should remain ridged from hip through knee to the retaining strap during application or force.)

5. Determine the mean value of the 3 maximal tensiometer measures and record this in the appropriate location.

6. Utilizing the table provided with the tensiometer to convert the mean tensiometer measure to a measure of force in kgs.

7. Determine maximal limb torque by multiplying the converted force measure (kgs.) (procedure 6) by the distance from the joint (cms.) (procedure 3). This torque measure of muscular strength is to be recorded on the subject's form.

PROCEDURES (Speed Tests)

1. Using the tape measures provided, on a level surface lay out the course to be run (10 meters and 40 meters).

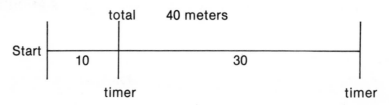

2. For each of three performances have the performer assume any comfortable starting position, behind the selected starting line.

3. Upon the starter's indication, the subject will begin from the starting line running as rapidly as possible the 40 meter distance.

4. Times for distances of 10 meters and 40 meters will be recorded as the subject passes the appropriate finish positions. These times should be recorded in the provided locations on your recording forms.

5. Subtract the 10 meter time from the 40 meter time to produce the time for the last 30 meters and record the results of this calculation in the appropriate location on your recording form.

6. Divide the time for the first 10 meters into the 10 meter distance to determine starting velocity, and the time for the remaining 30 meters into the 30 meter distance to determine running velocity. Record each of these in the appropriate locations on the recording form.

7. The highest velocity for each of the measures (10 meter distance and 30 meter distance) should be recorded as the subject's score for that measure.

PROCEDURES (Agility Test)

1. On the course provided and described below, have the subject assume any comfortable position behind the start-finish line.

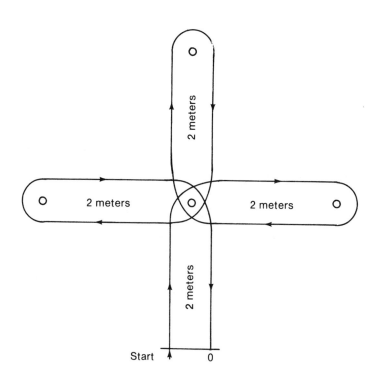

2. On the starter's signal, have the subject follow the described path to complete the agility test.

3. Each subject should perform the test 3 times with each time recorded in the appropriate location.

4. The fastest of the three times should be selected as the subject's score for the agility test.

PROCEDURES (Bent Arm Hang)

1. Lift the subject into a support position on the horizontal bar provided.
   (NOTE: The chin of the subject should be above the bar but not resting on it, the hands should be shoulder width, with lower arms pronated.)

2. Upon releasing the subject, start the timing of his/her performance.

3. Stop the time when any one of the following occurs:
   a. The chin rests on the bar, or
   b. any part of the subject's body touches a wall, floor or other support area or
   c. the subject's arms come to a complete extension.

4. Record the elapsed time for each of three trials in the areas provided.

5. The longest duration is the measure of the subject's muscular endurance and should be recorded in the appropriate location on the recording form.

PROCEDURES (Vertical Jump)

1. Have the subject assume a standing position with both feet in the area provided.

2. Without stepping, have the subject jump as high as possible with landing in the same area.

3. Record the elapsed time in the air in the space provided for each of three trials.

4. Using the conversion chart provided, convert the subject's non-support time to height jumped.

5. Multiply the subject's weight times the median height from the three trials to determine the power the subject was able to exert.

6. Record this measure in the appropriate location on his/her recording form.

NOTE: This test as described is conducted with a 1/1000 second timer (e.g. DEKAN model 1741) using a foot control plate as the jumping area. This test could be conducted by using a standard vertical jump and reach board.

SUBMISSION FORMS — Performance Evaluation

Name _____ Section_____

Strength Tests

Hip Hyperextension

Hip to retaining strap distance _____ cms.

Tensiometer readings

reading 1 _____ units

reading 2 _____ units

reading 3 _____ units   Mean _____ units

Conversion of tensiometer units to kgs. _____ kgs.

Hip hyperextension torque
Hip to retaining strap distance x kgs. of force = torque

_____ x _____ = _____

Elbow Flexion

Elbow to retaining strap distance _____ cms.

Tensiometer readings

reading 1 _____ units

reading 2 _____ units

reading 3 _____ units   Mean _____ units

Conversion of tensiometer units in kgs. _____ kgs.

Elbow flexion torque
Elbow to strap distance x kgs. of force = torque

_____ x _____ = _____

Agility Test

Trial 1 - time _____ sec.

Trial 2 - time _____ sec.

Trial 3 - time _____ sec.   Fastest Trial - time _____ sec.

Speed Tests

Trial 1

Time at 10 meters _____ sec.

Velocity for 10 meters _____ m/sec.

Time at 40 meters _____ sec.

Computed time for 10 to 40 meter distance _____ sec.

Velocity for 30 meter distance _____ m/sec.

Trial 2

    Time at 10 meters _____ sec.

      Velocity for 10 meters _____ m/sec.

    Time at 40 meters _____ sec.

    Computed time for 10 to 40 meter distance _____ sec.

      Velocity for 30 meter distance _____ m/sec.

Trial 3

    Time at 10 meters _____ sec.

      Velocity for 10 meters _____ m/sec.

    Time at 40 meters _____ sec.

    Computed time for 10 to 40 meter distance _____ sec.

      Velocity for 30 meter distance _____ m/sec.

Highest computed velocities for:

    10 meter distance _____ m/sec.

    30 meter distance _____ m/sec.

Bent Arm Hang Test

    Trial 1 - time _____ sec.

    Trial 2 - time _____ sec.

    Trial 3 - time _____ sec.   Longest time _____ sec.

Vertical Jump Test

    Trial 1

      Time in air _____ sec.   Computed height _____ cms.

    Trial 2

      Time in air _____ sec.   Computed height _____ cms.

    Trial 3

      Time in air _____ sec.   Computed height _____ cms.

    Median height jumped   _____ cms.

    Subject weight _____ kgs.

    Subject weight x height jumped = mechanical power

        _____ x _____ = _____ kgs - cms.

QUESTIONS

As a future coach, what value is there in knowing the relative performance measures of possible performers for your team. (Select two of those which you have conducted during this laboratory experience.)

measure _____

value _____

_____

_____

_____

_____

measure _____

value _____

_____

_____

_____

_____

In the evaluation of a person's general fitness, what performance measurements would you conduct? Why?

_____

_____

_____

_____

_____

_____

In conducting or observing the performance measurement procedures during your laboratory experience, where did you notice inaccuracies occurring? Why?

_____

_____

_____

_____

_____

_____

_____

RELATIONSHIPS

PURPOSE

To examine the relationships which exist between anthropometric and goniometric measures and the performance test results accumulated during your past three laboratory experiences.

To compare these relationships to your biases as indicated during your first laboratory session.

THEORY

Biases are imposed by every coach or physical education professional in their selection of teams or potential superior performers. The more substantial the base of information on which decisions are made, the smaller the bias which is imposed. It is therefore necessary to evaluate relationships among factors which could be important to a performance, hence eliminating the need for subjective selection of performers.

PROCEDURES

1. Obtain the results of the correlations among the variables concerned from your laboratory instructor.

2. Record those correlations by checking the appropriate locations on your submission forms.

3. Provide some possible explanation for the relationships which you now present as true relationships among the variables concerned.

4. Complete the laboratory submission forms by answering the supplied questions, prior to submission of the forms. These answers should: (a) relate your original estimates to the relationships found, (b) explain major differences which appeared, and (c) indicate how you could reduce your personal biases in the future.

SUBMISSION FORMS — Relationship Evaluation

Name _____ Section _____

Performance Variables	Anthropometric Variables	Negative −1	Relationship None 0	Positive +1
1. Hip Hyperextension Strength	Thigh circumference			
	Lower Leg volume			
	Leg length			
	Stature height			
	Total Body weight			
	Hip ROM hyperextension			

Explanation of the relationships found _____

_____

_____

Performance Variables	Anthropometric Variables	Negative −1	Relationship None 0	Positive +1
2. Elbow Flexion Strength	Upper Arm circumference			
	Lower Arm volume			
	Shoulder diameter			
	Stature height			
	Total Body weight			
	Wrist ROM flexion			

Explanation of the relationships found _____

_____

_____

Performance Variables	Anthropometric Variables	Negative −1	Relationship None 0	Positive +1

3. Agility

	Negative −1	None 0	Positive +1
Thigh circumference			
Leg and Foot volume			
Hip diameter			
Stature height			
Total Body weight			
Knee ROM flexion			

Explanation of the relationships found _____

_____

_____

_____

4. Starting Speed (10 meters)

	Negative −1	None 0	Positive +1
Thigh circumference			
Leg and Foot volume			
Hip diameter			
Stature height			
Total Body weight			
Ankle ROM flexion			

Explanation of the relationships found _____

_____

_____

_____

_____

Performance Variables	Anthropometric Variables	Negative −1	Relationship None 0	Positive +1
5. Running Speed (30 meters)	Thigh circumference			
	Leg and Foot volume			
	Hip diameter			
	Stature height			
	Total Body weight			
	Hip ROM hyperextension			

Explanation of the relationships found _____

_____

_____

_____

		Negative −1	None 0	Positive +1
6. Muscular Endurance (bent arm hang)	Upper Arm circumference			
	Arm and Hand volume			
	Shoulder diameter			
	Stature height			
	Total Body weight			
	Elbow ROM flexion			

Explanation of the relationships found _____

_____

_____

_____

Performance Variables	Anthropometric Variables	Negative −1	Relationship None 0	Positive +1
7. Power (vertical jump test)				
	Thigh circumference		|	
	Leg and Foot volume		|	
	Hip diameter		|	
	Leg length		|	
	Total Body weight		|	
	Knee ROM flexion		|	

Explanation of the relationships found _____

_____

_____

_____

Describe the major differences between the speculated relationships from your introductory session and the true relationships presented.

_____

_____

_____

_____

_____

_____

_____

_____

_____

_____

_____

_____

_____

_____

Why do you feel these differences appeared? _____

_____

_____

_____

_____

_____

_____

_____

_____

Explain how you personally could go about reducing biases when team selection is based on some performance skill variables. _____

_____

_____

_____

_____

_____

_____

_____

_____

ELECTROGONIOMETRY
analysis of the
normal walking stride

PURPOSE

To observe, estimate, and record selected joint motion in the performance of the normal walking stride.

THEORY

The electrogoniometer is a type of goniometer in which a potentiometer has been substituted for the protractor. Two movable arms are connected to the potentiometer and serve as positioning arms for attachment to limb segments. Motion of these arms causes motion of the potentiometer components which then act in much the same manner as a volume dial on a radio. Resistance to an electric current fed into the potentiometer is altered by the motion of the potentiometer components. If the device is properly calibrated, the electrical output to a recording device will represent angular motion effected about the axis of the potentiometer. While a manual goniometer is capable only of measuring joint angles in a stationary position, the electrogoniometer is able to record the continuous change in joint angle during motion.

Although the normal walking gait may be considered slow in comparison to other more athletic activities, it is, nonetheless, a highly complex motion involving the simultaneous coordinated movement of many joints and segments. As such, the task of making accurate estimates of the motion by eye is especially difficult.

In this laboratory experience, efforts will be made to estimate the angular motions of the knee and ankle joints during defined aspects of the walking stride. Based upon previous knowledge and measurements, we can establish with some accuracy the limiting ranges of motion possible at these joints. We can be fairly certain, as well, that angular positions of these joints during a normal walking stride will exist within these ranges. Electrogoniometric records will then be made of the flexion-hyperextension motions of the knee and ankle joints to afford comparisons between the estimated and recorded motions.

EQUIPMENT

Universal elgon attached to a chassis for the knee
Universal elgon attached to a chassis for the ankle
Elgon calibrating protractor
Elgon preamplifier
Recording device

REFERENCES

Adrian, M., Tipton, C. M., and Karpovich, P. V. **Electrogoniometry Manual.** Springfield College, Physiological Research Laboratory, (mimeographed), 1965.

Wells, K. F. and Luttgens, K. **Kinesiology: Scientific Basis of Human Motion.** 6th edition, Philadelphia: W. B. Saunders Company, 1976.

PROCEDURES

1. Based on your knowledge of the classification and degrees of freedom of each of the lower appendicular joints (knee and ankle), determine the active ranges of motion for the flexion-hyperextension movements of these joints.

2. Locate and mark on the right edge of each appropriate graph paper provided the limiting ranges of motion you have determined. Use the larger of your measures (flexion-hyperextension) as the upper or lower respective extreme and set the other direction to the appropriate scale. The scale for each graph may be different and will be determined by the extent of motion at that joint.

3. Through observation, estimate the angular position of each joint (knee and ankle) in the flexion — hyperextension motion for each of the six described aspects of the normal walking stride. (NOTE: heel strike repeats at both 0 and 100 percent of the total stride.) Plot a small point which represents you or your group's estimate of the scaled joint position at that particular aspect of the stride.

4. Connect the plotted points with a smooth curved line across the graph to illustrate the joint movement for the complete stride.

5. Calibration, Attachment, and Operation of the Elgons:

    a. In calibrating the elgons, two factors are of paramount importance. First, the recordings must accurately display the extreme limits of the motions. Second, the elgon must accurately record varying increments of that motion within the extremes. Attach the elgon to a protractor and establish a baseline (180 degrees on elgon equals the zero point on the recording paper). Move the elgon arms to the extreme limits anticipated from the walking motion. Adjust the sensitivity of the recording device to record a scaled value of those extreme positions. Return the elgon to the zero position and adjust the centering dial on the recorder so that the pen returns to the baseline. Repeat this operation, adjusting the centering and sensitivity dials, until the limits of the motion are accurately displayed.

    b. With the elgon still attached to the protractor, move the elgon arms in ten (10) degree increments throughout the expected range of motion. Continue adjusting the sensitivity setting until accurate displays on the recording device are achieved for both the limits of the motion and the increments within those limits.

    c. Repeat the calibration procedure for the other elgon.

    d. Identify the axis of motion for the knee joint. With the subject standing erect, draw a line with a skin pencil from the greater trochanter of the femur to the lateral epicondyle of the femur. Draw another line from the lateral epicondyle of the femur to the lateral malleolus of the ankle.

e. Place the arms of the electrogoniometer along the lines drawn on the limb segments (mechanical axes) with the potentiometer centered over the axis of rotation of the knee joint. Secure the elgon in this position.

f. Identify the axis of motion for the ankle joint. Draw light lines on the subject from the center of the lateral malleolus of the ankle to the proximal head of the fifth metatarsal and from the lateral malleolus to the lateral epicondyle of the femur.

g. Place the arms of the ankle elgon along the lines on the limb segments (mechanical axes) with the potentiometer centered over the lateral malleolus (joint axis).

h. Have your subject stand in a normal resting position and center the recording line at the zero position on the flexion-hyperextension scale. Movements now will illustrate deviations from this base position.

i. Record electrogoniographs of the knee and ankle motion during the normal walking stride.

6. Attach the electrogoniographs in the appropriate places on the laboratory submission forms.

7. Describe the differences you observed between your estimations and the recordings of the knee and ankle motions and spectulate on the reasons for these differences.

SUBMISSION FORMS — Electrogoniometry

Name _____ Section _____

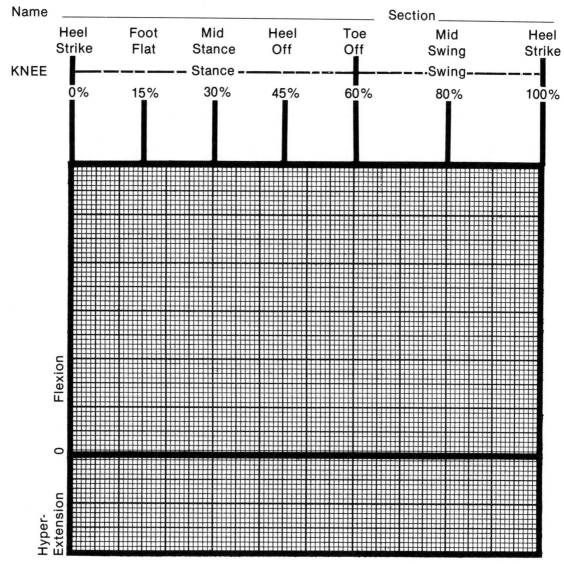

	Heel Strike	Foot Flat	Mid Stance	Heel Off	Toe Off	Mid Swing	Heel Strike
KNEE	0%	15%	30%	45%	60%	80%	100%

Place the electrogoniometric recording of the Knee motion of your subject in the space below.

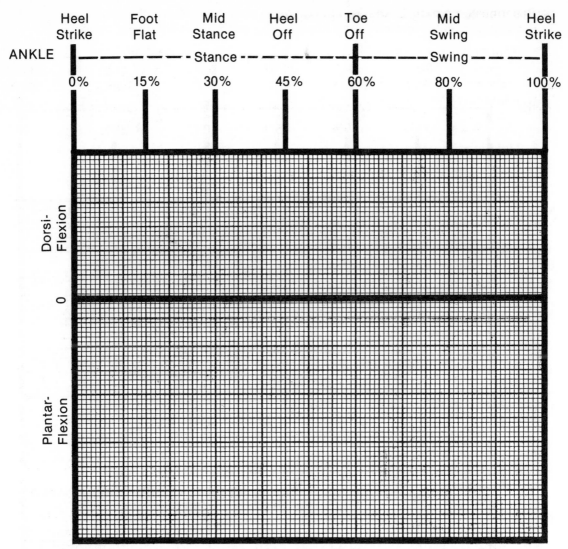

ANKLE

Place the electrogoniometric recording of the Ankle motion of your subject in the space below.

1. Describe the noticeable variations between your estimation and the recording of the actual angular motion of the knee during each of the following phases:

   a. Heel Strike to Foot Flat _____

   _____

   b. Foot Flat to Mid Stance _____

   _____

   c. Mid Stance to Heel Off _____

   _____

   d. Heel Off to Toe Off _____

   _____

   e. Toe Off to Mid Swing _____

   _____

   f. Mid Swing to Heel Strike _____

   _____

2. Speculate on the reasons for the differences between your estimations and the recording of actual angular motions of the knee during the observed walking strides.

   _____

   _____

   _____

   _____

   _____

   _____

3. Describe the noticeable variations between your estimation and the recording of the actual angular motion of the ankle during each of the following phases:

   a. Heel Strike to Foot Flat _____

   _____

   b. Foot Flat to Mid Stance _____

   _____

   c. Mid Stance to Heel Off _____

   _____

   d. Heel Off to Toe Off _____

   _____

   e. Toe Off to Mid Swing _____

   _____

   f. Mid Swing to Heel Strike _____

   _____

4. Speculate on the reasons for the differences between your estimations and the recording of actual angular motions of the ankle during the observed walking strides.

_____

_____

_____

_____

_____

_____

ELECTROMYOGRAPHY
analysis of
muscular contraction

PURPOSE

To determine the magnitude and duration of the activity of a muscular group during the performance of a selected activity. Both of these factors may be determined through the subjective evaluation of electromyographic recordings.

THEORY

Electromyography is an evaluative technique based on the discovery by Galvoni in the late Eighteenth Century that muscular contractions are produced by the propagation of electrical impulses along muscular tissue.

The structural unit of contraction is the muscle cell, or muscle fiber, which may have a length up to 30mm and is less than 0.1mm wide. In mammalian muscle, small groups of fibers contract at the same time. These small groups of fibers are called motor units. Each motor unit is supplied by the terminal branches of one nerve fiber (or axon) whose cell body is located in the anterior horn of the spinal cord's gray matter. A nervous impulse causes all muscle fibers in the unit to contract almost simultaneously. Many motor units are involved in a strong muscular contraction. The motor units act asynchronously and result in a smooth development of tension in the overall muscle.

When the motor neuron impulse stimulates a motor unit, it causes a brief twitch, followed by rapid and complete relaxation. The duration of the twitch is approximately 1 to 2 milliseconds. All the fibers in the motor unit do not contract at exactly the same time; some are delayed for several milliseconds. A minute electrical potential is generated by the twitch, and then it dissipates into the surrounding tissues. This electrical potential developed by the twitch of all the fibers in the motor unit is spread out over 5 to 12 milliseconds. The electrical result is an electrical discharge with a median duration of 9 milliseconds and a total amplitude of about 0.5 mV.

This is called a motor unit potential (MUP). It looks like a sharp spike and is most often biphasic, although it may be more complex (triphasic or multiphasic). Usually the larger the MUP, the larger the motor unit which has produced it. The size of the MUP recorded will vary with respect to the distance of the motor unit from the electrodes, the type of electrode used (surface, needle, fine-wire, etc.), and the type of recording device used.

In the recruitment of motor units, the smaller motor unit potentials appear first, this occurs with only a very slight contraction. As the force of the contraction is increased, larger motor units are recruited and larger MUPs are observed. Simultaneously, all motor units recruited increase their frequency of firing. These factors appear to defend the "size theory of motor unit recruitment" which has been presented by some researchers.

SIMULATED RECORDING OF A BIPHASIC MOTOR UNIT POTENTIAL SPIKE

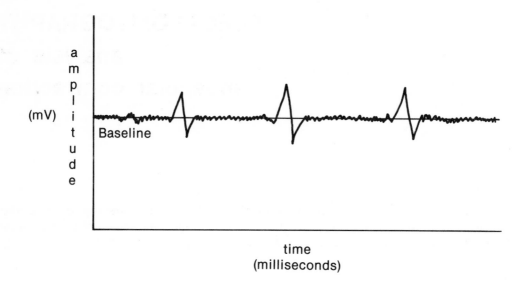

EQUIPMENT

Surface electrodes and collars
Electrode paste
Skin preparation materials
Skin marking pencils
Recording device
Muscle stimulator

REFERENCES

Basmajian, J. V. **Muscles Alive.** 3rd edition, Baltimore: The Williams and Wilkins Co., 1974.

O'Connell, A. L. and Gardner, E. B. **Understanding the Scientific Bases of Human Movement.** Baltimore: The Williams and Wilkins Co., 1972.

PROCEDURES

1. Based on the drawing below, locate the motor point, reference point, and grounding point (boney landmark) for evaluation of the muscular activity of the biceps brachii. Mark these three points with the skin marking pencil provided.
   NOTE: location of the motor point can be done through muscle stimulation on all subjects, this procedure if provided will be conducted by your instructor.

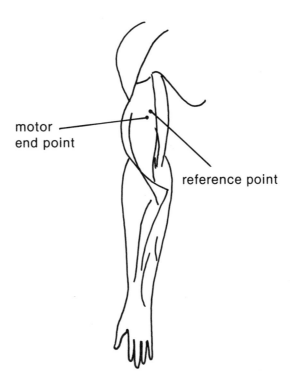

motor
end point

reference point

2. Prepare the skin over the three marked points to increase the electrical conductivity in these areas. This process requires the removal of skin oils with either alcohol or acetone, and the removal of dead skin cells by rubbing the skin firmly with a rough towel or fine sandpaper.

3. Place an adhesive collar on each of the required electrodes. Fill the electrodes with electrode paste until it is even with the edge of the collar (this paste enhances the skin to electrode conductivity). Peel the protective cover from the collar and place the electrodes on the skin at the three prepared points.

4. Secure each electrode and the associated wires to the subject's arm with adhesive tape so that they are not pulled away from the skin during the performance.

5. Attach the three wires to their appropriate plug positions, this attachment will allow the impulses to be recorded.

6. As the subject is performing the selected movement, manually or electronically, mark the recording which is being produced indicating the time when the beginning, midpoint, and ending of the concentric and eccentric motions occur.

7. Attach a recording of at least one complete movement at the specified position on your laboratory submission form.

8. Label the electromyographic recording indicating those portions of the recording which take place during the concentric phase and those portions which take place during the eccentric phase.

9. Label the lines which represent the raw electromyographic recording, the integrated electromyographic recording (if available) and the marks which indicate the beginning and ending of the various phases of the motion.

10. Evaluate the concentric portion of the recording by providing the required answers to questions dealing with that portion of the stride.

11. Evaluate the eccentric portion of the recording by providing the required answers to questions dealing with that portion of the stride.

12. Based on your evaluations, draw the required comparisons and conclusions to complete the laboratory submission forms.

Name _____ Section _____

Electromyographic Recording

place your recording here

Answer the following questions in relation to the recording of the concentric phase:

1. Is the muscle active during this phase? _____

2. At what point during this phase does the muscle appear to be most active?

    _____

3. Is the muscle shortening or lengthening during this phase?

    _____

4. is the muscle contracting ballisticly or non-ballisticly during this phase?

    _____

5. What type of contraction is being performed during this phase? (isometric, isotonic, or isokinetic) _____

_____

Answer the following questions in relation to the recording of the eccentric phase:

1. Is the muscle active during this phase? _____

2. At what point during this phase does the muscle appear to be most active?

_____

3. Is the muscle shortening or lengthening during this phase?

_____

4. Is the muscle contracting ballisticly or non-ballisticly during this phase?

_____

5. What type of contraction is performed during this phase? (isometric, isotonic, or isokinetic) _____

_____

What difficulties did you encounter during the preparation or recording phase of the experience?

_____

_____

_____

_____

What difficulties did you encounter during the evaluation of the recording for this experience?

_____

_____

_____

_____

Were you able to discern the recruitment of motor units from your recording?

_____

Were you able to select the multiple occurrence of a particular MUP spike from your recording? If so, circle these spikes on the recording.

_____

What similarities can be detected in the concentric and eccentric phases of your performance? Why? _____

_____

_____

_____

_____

_____

_____

_____

What effect does recruitment have and what is the reason for the MUP spikes?

_____

_____

_____

_____

_____

_____

_____

KINESTHESIS
movement reproducibility
and
skill level

PURPOSE

To evaluate the gross motor kinesthetic perception of a performer through the use of flexometric, goniometric and dynametric procedures, and to determine if there is a relationship between these measures of kinesthetic perception and the performance of a selected closed system motor skill.

THEORY

Kinesthesis deals with the perception of an individual's muscular movement and the relative position of the body's parts in space. This perception is accomplished through subconscious evaluation of impulses received from sensors present in the tissues directly associated with the muscles, tendons, and joints. These sensors are collectively termed proprioceptors and are responsible for a continuous flow of impulses which upon integration produce information used to form appropriate response patterns. The primary propriceptors responsible for our gross motor kinesthetic sense of limb and joint motions are the muscle spindle and the golgi tendon organ. A diagramatic and/or verbal description of these proprioceptors will be requested later in this laboratory experience.

The factor of kinesthesis or the kinesthetic sense may be considered of value in the performance of many closed system movement skills. Many of these skills require no particular ability in a given sport except that needed to reproduce a successful performance many times in succession. The kicking of fieldgoals in football, the shooting of free-throws in basketball, or the movement required to achieve a strike in bowling may be considered to be included in this category of movement. With this theory in mind, the performer who can assume the same position and perform the same movements with a similar quantity of muscular activity as a previously successful performance will achieve subsequent success while those who are not capable of this reproduction of motion will, in fact, not be successful.

EQUIPMENT

Flexometers
Floor targets
Goniometers
Opaque screen
Spring scales
Tennis balls

REFERENCES

Clarke, D. H. **Exercise Physiology.** Englewood Cliffs, N.J.: Prentice-Hall, Inc., 1975.

Karpovich, P. V. and Sinning, W. E. **Physiology of Muscular Activity.** 7th edition, Philadelphia: W. B. Saunders Company, 1971.

Wells, K. F. and Luttgens, K. **Kinesiology: Scientific Basis of Human Motion.** 6th edition, Philadelphia: W. B. Saunders Company, 1976.

HYPOTHESES

1. There will be no significant relationship between the measure of wrist angle variability and the performance of a selected closed system motor skill.

2. There will be no significant relationship between the measure of elbow angle variability and the performance of a selected closed system motor skill.

3. There will be no significant relationship between the measure of muscular tension variability and the performance of a selected closed system motor skill.

PROCEDURES

1. On the submission form, complete the required verbal and diagramatic descriptions of the proprioceptors, and the required definitions.

2. On the submission form, record the required information pertaining to your subject. (NOTE: every member of your laboratory group will perform these observations on a different subject.)

3. Position the supplied flexometer on the lower arm of your subject as diagrammed below. Be sure the long axis of the flexometer coincides with the mechanical axis of the segment.

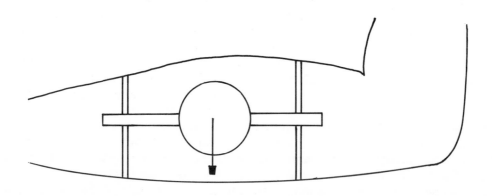

4. Have your subject assume a sitting position at the measurement table with his/her throwing arm in the position diagrammed below. In this position, use the flexometer to evaluate the elbow angle and the goniometer to evaluate the angle of the wrist. Record your readings on the submission forms.

5. Have your subject return to a relaxed position with the elbow and wrist extended, then have him/her return to the throwing position which they had previously assumed. (NOTE: no feedback is to be given during these measurement trials.) Repeat this procedure nine times recording your measurements in trials 2 through 10 on your submission form.

6. Based on your 10 angular measures, calculate the mean, range and standard deviation for each of the two joint angles. Note that the smaller the standard deviation measure is, the better your subject was able to reproduce his/her original position.

7. Have your subject perform a muscular tension trial using the spring scale while attempting to exert a force of 1000 grams (1 kg.). After attempting to hold this exact tension for 3 seconds, record his/her end reading on the submission forms.

8. Have your subject return to the resting position and then attempt to reproduce the approximate 1000 gram (1 kg.) muscular tension which he had previously performed. Repeat this procedure 9 times recording your measures on the submission form trials 2 through 10. (NOTE: no feedback is to be given during these 9 trials.)

9. Based on your 10 muscular tension measures, calculate the mean, range and standard deviation. Note that the smaller the standard deviation measure is, the better your subject was able to reproduce the original tension.

10. Have your subject perform the selected closed motor skill, as described below, (with visual feedback), until two **consecutive** scores of 3 are achieved. Then (without

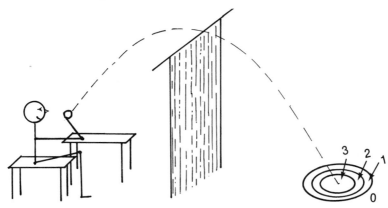

feedback) allow him/her to perform 10 more trials of the closed motor skill. Record the scores for each trial on the submission form.

11. Determine the total number of points obtained on the selected closed system motor skill by summing the scores from each of the 10 trials. Note that the higher this score is, the better you have performed the selected skill.

12. Determine if you feel that there is a relationship between your ability to reproduce positions or tensions and your ability to perform a selected closed motor task.

13. Based on your determinations, evaluate the three hypotheses previously listed. Your evaluation will be in the form of a TRUE or FALSE response.

14. Based on your hypotheses evaluations, answer the question dealing with the relationship between your kinesthetic sense and your ability to reproduce a position, motion or tension.

15. Discuss the implications of your findings as they relate to other more conventional sport performances.

Name _____ Section _____

DEFINE

Closed Motor Skill _____

_____

_____

_____

DESCRIBE

Muscle Spindle _____

_____

_____

Golgi Tendon Organ _____

_____

_____

COMPLETE THE DIAGRAM

One the diagram of a muscle spindle, match the correct letter to each of the following labels:

_____ Flower spray ending
_____ Extrafusal fibers
_____ Intrafusal endings
_____ Annulospiral endings
_____ Efferent neurons
_____ Afferent neurons

Muscle Spindle

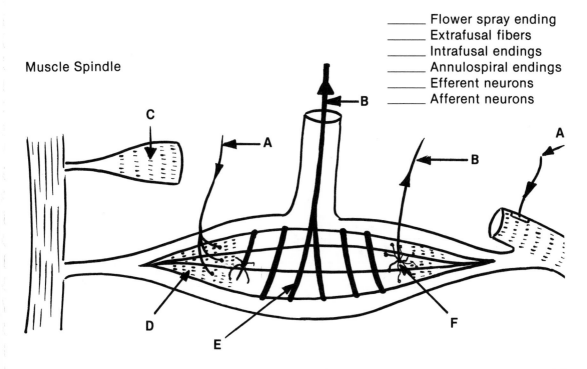

Flexometric and Goniometric Measures

Trial	Wrist Angle	Elbow Angle
1.		
2.		
3.		
4.		
5.		
6.		
7.		
8.		
9.		
10.		
Mean		
Range		
S. D.		

Trial	Muscular Tension
1.	
2.	
3.	
4.	
5.	
6.	
7.	
8.	
9.	
10.	
Mean	
Range	
S. D.	

Closed Motor Skill Performance Scores

Trial	Score
1.	
2.	
3.	
4.	
5.	
6.	
7.	
8.	
9.	
10.	
Sum	

Summary of Required Information

Wrist angle standard deviation _____ . _____ degrees

Elbow angle standard deviation _____ . _____ degrees

Muscular tension standard deviation _____ . _____ grams

Performance score sum _____ . points

EVALUATIONS OF HYPOTHESES

Test of Hypothesis 1 (circle)   TRUE   FALSE

Test of Hypothesis 2 (circle)   TRUE   FALSE

Test of Hypothesis 3 (circle)   TRUE   FALSE

Does there appear to be a relationship between kinesthetic sense and motor performance (based on your evaluation of the hypotheses.)?

_____

_____

_____

_____

_____

_____

_____

_____

_____

Implications of your findings to more common closed sport skills.

_____

_____

_____

_____

_____

_____

_____

_____

_____

How is vision considered a factor in the feedback loop and what influence does it have?

_____

_____

_____

_____

_____

Explain the practice effect in relation to aquisition of a new skill and why is "perfect" practice so important? _____

_____

_____

_____

_____

_____

EXERCISE DEVICE
EVALUATION

PURPOSE

To allow you to evaluate a "gimmick" exercise device based on your knowledge of basic kinesiological concepts.

To allow for a thorough review of anatomically oriented kinesiological concepts near the end of your instruction in this information.

THEORY

The uninformed consumer has become the primary target for disreputable manufacturers in many areas. The physical education and fitness areas are not isolated from this influx.

"Gimmick" exercise devices have appeared on the market in great numbers in recent years. These exercisers provide claims which range from those based on logical well founded scientific theory to gross exaggeration of expected outcomes.

With the present overabundance of these devices, concerned consumers have begun to question the value of these "gimmicks" in general, and more specifically the cost to value ratio for those devices which tend to be more expensive.

Within the realm of the physical educator should be the information necessary to make knowledgeable evaluations of the general and specific values of these devices. These evaluations will be requested and expected by your students, and you as a physical educator should be able to provide this information.

EQUIPMENT

A selected "gimmick" exercise device.

REFERENCES

Broer, M. **Efficiency of Human Movement.** Philadelphia: W. B. Saunders, Co., 1973.

Cooper, J. and Glassow, R. **Kinesiology.** St. Louis: C. V. Mosby Co., 1976.

Gray, H. **Anatomy of the Human Body.** ed. C. M. Goss, Philadelphia: W. B. Saunders, Co., 1974.

Karpovich, P. V. and Sinning, W. E. **Physiology of Muscular Activity.** 7th ed. Philadelphia: W. B. Saunders, Co., 1971.

Kelley, D. L. **Kinesiology: Fundamentals of Motion Description.** Englewood Cliffs, N.J.: Prentice-Hall, Inc., 1971.

DEFINITION

"Gimmick" exercise device — a "gimmick" exercise device is a commonly and commercially available inexpensive (maximum $40) device which makes claims consistent with the benefits derived from any exercise or exercise program. The device should provide these above mentioned benefits as the only significant outcome of their use.

PROCEDURES

1. Select a "gimmick" exercise device and inform your instructor of your choice. (Duplication of device will not be permitted within a laboratory session.)

2. Select one particular exercise which you feel can provide a beneficial result or results which can not be achieved without any device.

3. On the submission form provided, complete the following information about your selected exerciser:
   a. the commercial name of your "gimmick" exerciser.
   b. the commercial manufacture of your "gimmick" exerciser.
   c. the approximate price of your "gimmick" exerciser.
   d. the method or mechanical principle by which the device provides resistance to movement.

4. On the submission form provided, complete the following information about your selected exercise:
   a. the name of the exercise you are evaluating.
   b. a verbal description of your selected exercise using appropriate kinesiological terminology.
   c. the suggested objectives of performaing your selected exercise.
   d. the names of the agonistic muscle(s) or muscular group(s) which are active during the performance of your exercise.
   e. the names of the antagonistic muscle(s) or muscular group(s).
   f. the type of agonistic muscular contraction required during your exercise (isometric, isotonic, or isokinetic), and the reason why you feel this type of contraction is required.
   g. the direction of the agonistic muscular contraction (concentric or eccentric).
   h. the ballisticity of the agonistic muscular contraction (ballistic or non-ballistic).
   i. the reason why your exercise meets the suggested objective.
   j. the reason why your exercise meets your suggested objective **better** than **any** exercise which required no external object or device.

5. Based on your evaluation, prepare a demonstration and presentation of your exerciser and exercise for your classmates (approximately 5 minutes) as if you were attempting to sell this device. (Be prepared to answer critical questions about your exerciser.)

6. While observing the other sales presentations, evaluate the cost to value ratio and indicate if this ratio is appropriate for you to suggest the purchase of this device. (You should plan to ask questions in order to be able to make knowledgeable judgements.)

SUBMISSION FORMS — Exercise Device Evaluation

Name _____ Section _____

"GIMMICK" EXERCISER EVALUATION

Name of "gimmick" exerciser _____

Manufacture _____

Approximate price - (Max. $40.00) _____

Method of resistance production _____

_____

_____

SELECTED EXERCISE

Name of exercise _____

Verbal description of exercise _____

_____

_____

_____

_____

_____

Suggested objective of performing this exercise _____

_____

_____

_____

Agonistic muscles or muscular group(s) _____

_____

Antagonistic muscles or muscular group(s) _____

_____

Type of agonistic contraction required _____

Why is that type required _____

_____

_____

_____

_____

_____

Direction of agonistic muscular contraction _____

Ballisticity of agonistic muscular contraction _____

Why does this exercise meet your suggested objectives _____

_____

_____

_____

_____

_____

Why does your exercise meet your suggested objectives better than any exercise using no external object or device? (Why is it worthy of purchasing this exercise?)

_____

_____

_____

_____

_____

_____

_____

_____

_____

_____

_____

Using appropriate kinesiological terminology, provide a description of the primary motions of the exercise. Include (1) planes, (2) axes, (3) joint motions and (4) muscle(s) associated with each. _____

_____

_____

_____

_____

_____

_____

_____

_____

_____

_____

_____

SALES PRESENTATION EVALUATION

Device Name & Presenter's Name	Cost	Cost to Value Ratio					Would I Buy	
		1	2	3	4	5	yes	no
		( )	( )	( )	( )	( )	( )	( )
		( )	( )	( )	( )	( )	( )	( )
		( )	( )	( )	( )	( )	( )	( )
		( )	( )	( )	( )	( )	( )	( )
		( )	( )	( )	( )	( )	( )	( )
		( )	( )	( )	( )	( )	( )	( )
		( )	( )	( )	( )	( )	( )	( )
		( )	( )	( )	( )	( )	( )	( )
		( )	( )	( )	( )	( )	( )	( )
		( )	( )	( )	( )	( )	( )	( )
		( )	( )	( )	( )	( )	( )	( )
		( )	( )	( )	( )	( )	( )	( )
		( )	( )	( )	( )	( )	( )	( )
		( )	( )	( )	( )	( )	( )	( )
		( )	( )	( )	( )	( )	( )	( )
		( )	( )	( )	( )	( )	( )	( )
		( )	( )	( )	( )	( )	( )	( )
		( )	( )	( )	( )	( )	( )	( )
		( )	( )	( )	( )	( )	( )	( )
		( )	( )	( )	( )	( )	( )	( )

Cost to Value Ratio
   1-No value
   2-Poor value
   3-Average value
   4-Good value
   5-Excellent value

MUSCULAR FORCE ANALYSIS
link system

PURPOSE

To evaluate the forces applied in resistance to a system of body links while those links remain in a static position.

To evaluate the true muscular force required to counter-balance a selected resistance.

To determine what relationship, if any, exists between required true muscular force and a selected measure of muscular endurance.

THEORY

The analysis of total body motion or total body position is a complex task often only possible by analysis of the action of the body's many constituent parts. One traditional method of partitioning the body is by segmental division. In this method, we assess position and motion by reference to the body's underlying skeletal structure. Muscles originate and insert upon this structure and by their contraction cause forces to be applied to it. If those forces possess sufficient magnitude to overcome all resistances to them, motion is capable of occurring.

Most of the segments in the human body are rigid structures bounded by a joint (or joints). Muscular forces about these joints can cause the segmental structure to rotate. In complex movements, and in many apparently simple ones, several segments must operate in concert with one another to accomplish that motion or to maintain a position in support of that motion.

One benefit of a segmental consideration of the human body is its relationship to simple lever mechanics. Because of this relationship, we are capable of evaluating characteristics of the motions and positions of the body segments. In this system, the major segmental bone provides the lever bar and the bounding joint capsule provides the fulcrum by acting as the axis of rotation. Effort forces are represented by the vector expressions of muscle attachments to the segments. The effect of gravity upon the segments as well as the imposition of external loads upon those segments represent the forces in resistance to the effort. Previous research has shown that segmental weight caused by the effect of gravity may be accurately conceived as a proportion of total body weight. (Dempster, 1955)

By determining the exact structure of a segment as it is held in a particular position, and by relying upon the lever arrangement described by that structure, vector analysis of the system can provide data representative of the real muscular force required to have the segment maintain its position. In many situations, the available muscular force does not attach to the major segmental bone at 90 degrees. In these cases, the desirable rotary effects of muscular contraction are diminished. Some of the muscular effort will provide a rotational component and some will provide a non-rotational or stabilizing component. These components and the vector representing the actual muscular force will exist in the normal trigonometric relationships of the right triangle.

This laboratory experience will provide the student with sufficient information to calculate the component vectors inherent to a particular anatomical structure when that structure is maintained in two specific positions. The anatomical structure will be the arm and the specific positions it will maintain will be 90 and 45 degrees of shoulder abduction. For this laboratory experience, assumption will be made that the major muscular force generated to maintain the positions of shoulder abduction will be provided by the medial deltoid muscle. When the actual muscular force required of this muscle is calculated, it will be correlated to the amount of time that force can be produced. The duration of this muscular force generation will be defined here as a measure of muscular endurance.

EQUIPMENT

Rulers   External loads
Stop watches   Skin marking pencils

REFERENCES

Dempster, W. "Space Requirements of the Seated Operator", **WADC Technical Report 55-158.** July, 1955, Wright Air Development Center, Air Research and Development Command, USAF, Wright-Patterson Air Force Base, Ohio.

Hay, J. G. **The Biomechanics of Sports Techniques.** 1st edition, pp. 107-122, Englewood Cliffs, New Jersey: Prentice-Hall, Inc., 1973.

Kelley, D. L. **Kinesiology: Fundamentals of Motion Description.** Englewood Cliffs, New Jersey: Prentice-Hall, Inc., 1971.

Wells, K. F. and Luttgens, K. **Kinesiology: Scientific Basis of Human Motion.** pp. 308-316, Philadelphia: W. B. Saunders Company, 1976.

HYPOTHESES

1. There will be no significant difference between the muscular forces (calculated) for 90 degree upper-arm abduction and for 45 degree upper-arm abduction.

2. There will be no significant difference between the muscular endurance measures for 90 degree upper-arm abducting and 45 degree abduction of the upper-arm link.

3. There will be no significant relationship between muscular force (calculated) and a measure of muscular endurance when the upper-arm link is held in a static position of 90 or 45 degrees.

PROCEDURES

1. The measurements required for this laboratory experience will be taken with you or a member of your laboratory team as the subject.

2. Have a member of your laboratory team locate the following anatomical landmarks, marking them lightly with a skin pencil:

   a. Greater tubercle of the humerus   c. Styloid process of the ulna
   b. Head of the radius   d. Distal end of the third phalange

3. Measure the three required segmental lengths deliniated by the above anatomical landmarks, which are required for further calculation. Record those measurements on Recording Form 1.

4. Calculate the weights (forces) of the segments which make up this system of links. These calculations will be based on the total body weight of the subject and constant proportions determined from cadaver dissection (Dempster, 1955). Upon performing the required calculations, record your results on Recording Form 2.

5. Calculate the positions of weight (force) applications on this link system in relation to the glenoid-humeral joint (fulcrum for the lever system). These calculations are based on the previously determined segmental lengths (Procedure 3) and on the constant proportions determined by cadaver dissection (Dempster, 1955). Record your results on Recording Form 3 distances, 2, 3 and 4. Distance 1, the distance from the glenoid-humeral joint to the deltoid tuberosity may be estimated from your upper arm length by the calculation described on Recording Form 3.

6. Transpose the weight and position (distance) information which you have just calculated to the Link System Diagrams and Calculation Summary Tables 1 and 2.

7. Determine the required information to complete the Calculation Summary Tables for both 90 degree shoulder abduction and 45 degree shoulder abduction.

8. Transpose the muscular force **magnitude** values from the calculation summary tables to the spaces provided for this information on the Submission Forms.

9. Assume a standing position with one arm in each of the following positions:

   a. Dominant arm — 45 degree shoulder abduction
            palm down
            prescribed weight in hand
               (men - 5 kgs.)
               (women - 2 kgs.)

   b. Non-dominant arm — 90 degree shoulder abduction
            palm down

10. Hold the assumed position until fatique occurs (hold each arm until fatique occurs in its medial deltoid, then continue with the other arm until fatique occurs in that arm).

11. Record the times in seconds until fatique requires that these positions can no longer be held in the spaces provided for this information on Submission Forms.

12. Follow the procedures described by your laboratory instructor to verify the correctness of your hand computations of muscular effort and for the determination of the required information for hypothesis testing.

13. Determine from your results, if you think the hypotheses tested were true or false. Base your implications of the laboratory experience on your evaluation of the presented hypotheses.

SUBMISSION FORMS — Muscular Force Analysis

NAME _____ SECTION _____

Link System Diagram 1 — 90 degree shoulder abduction

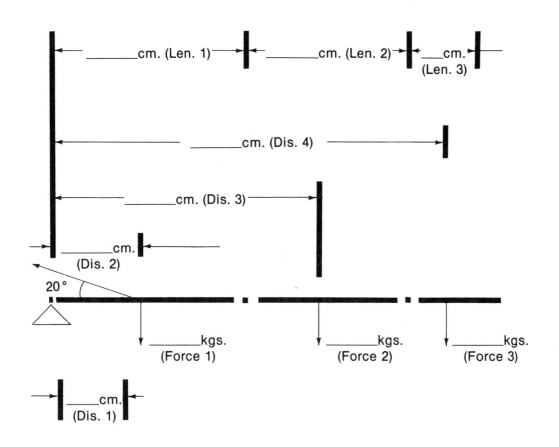

Calculation Summary Table 1 — 90 degree shoulder abduction

Forces	Magnitude	Distance	Rotational Component	Force Moment	Non-rotational Component
Upper Arm Wt.	(Force 1)	(Dis. 2)			
Lower Arm Wt.	(Force 2)	(Dis. 3)			
Hand Wt.	(Force 3)	(Dis. 4)			
Muscular Force		(Dis. 1)			
TOTAL	_____	_____	_____	0	

NOTE: Use the diagram at the top of the page to assist you in completing the above table.

Link System Diagram 2 — 45 degree shoulder abduction

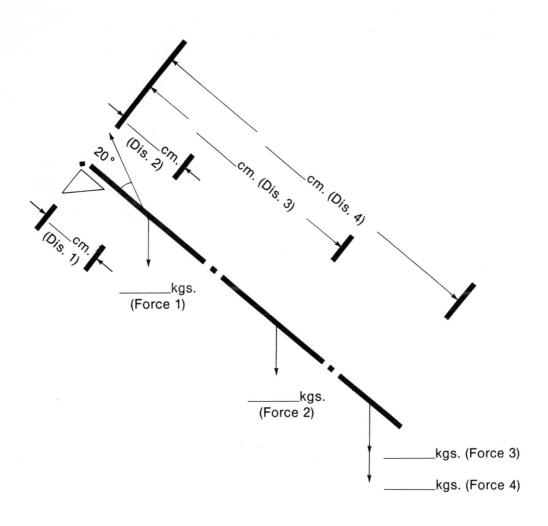

_____kgs.
(Force 1)

_____kgs.
(Force 2)

_____kgs. (Force 3)

_____kgs. (Force 4)

Calculation Summary Table 2 — 45 degree shoulder abduction

Forces	Magnitude	Distance	Rotational Component	Force Moment	Non-rotational Component
Upper Arm Wt.	(Force 1)	(Dis. 2)			
Lower Arm Wt.	(Force 2)	(Dis. 3)			
Hand Wt.	(Force 3)	(Dis. 4)			
Object Wt.	(Force 4)	(Dis. 4)			
Muscular Force					
TOTAL	_____	_____	_____	0	

RECORDING FORM 1 — SEGMENTAL LENGTHS

Length 1 = Greater tubercle of humerus to Head of Radius = _____ . _____ cms.

Length 2 = Head of radius to Styloid process of ulna = _____ . _____ cms.

Length 3 = Styloid process of ulna to Distal end of the third phalange =

_____ . _____ cms.

RECORDING FORM 2 — SEGMENTAL WEIGHTS (FORCES)

Subject Weight = _____ . _____ kgs.

Force 1 = Upper Arm Weight = Subject Weight × .027 = _____ . _____ kgs.

Force 2 = Lower Arm Weight = Subject Weight × .016 = _____ . _____ kgs.

Force 3 = Hand Weight = Subject Weight × .006 = _____ . _____ kgs.

Force 4 = Object Weight = _____ . _____ kgs.

RECORDING FORM 3 — FORCE APPLICATION DISTANCES

Distance 1 = Distance to deltoid tuberosity

= Length 1 x .405 = _____ . _____ cms.

Distance 2 = Distance to upper arm center of gravity

= Length 1 x .436 = _____ . _____ cms.

Distance 3 = Distance to lower arm center of gravity

= Length 1 + (Length 2 x .430) = _____ . _____ cms.

Distance 4 = Distance to hand (and object if any) center of gravity

= Length 1 + Length 2 + (Length 3 x .506) = _____ . _____ cms.

Calculated True Muscular Forces

Muscular force magnitude 90 degree abduction = _____ . _____ kgs.

Muscular force magnitude 45 degree abduction = _____ . _____ kgs.

Time Until Fatique (Muscular Endurance)

Time held at 90 degrees abduction = _____ sec.

Time held at 45 degrees abduction = _____ sec.

Results of Laboratory Experience — Evaluation of Hypotheses

Test for hypothesis 1 (circle)	TRUE	FALSE
Test for hypothesis 2 (circle)	TRUE	FALSE
Test for hypothesis 3 (circle)	TRUE	FALSE

Implications of Laboratory Experience Results

_____

_____

_____

_____

_____

_____

_____

_____

How does the relationship of muscular force to gravity determine the occurrence of isometric or isotonic contractions? _____

_____

_____

_____

_____

_____

CENTER OF GRAVITY
cinematographic and balance board methods

PURPOSE

To calculate the total body center of gravity by cinematographical segmental analysis.

To calculate the total body center of gravity by the direct balance board method.

To compare subjectively the results of these calculations with population norms.

Population Norms
Men · 55 to 57 percent of standing height in the anatomical position
Women · 53 to 55 percent of standing height in the anatomical position

THEORY

The center of gravity or the center of mass of a body is the theoretical point about which the mass of that body is evenly distributed. In the human body, the location of this theoretical point will depend upon several factors. It will depend upon how the varied segmental masses are distributed about the body and it will depend upon the specific location of those segments.

Just as the distribution of segmental masses will differ for any two persons, they will also differ between males and females. This will cause the locations of the theoretical total body centers of gravity to differ. In 1955, Dempster conducted research on cadavers to establish how the total body mass was distributed among its segments. From his work, we are able to calculate the specific masses of each of the body's segments if we know the total mass of the body.

As the body changes position or reorients itself in its environment, it will cause the distribution of its segmental masses to change in relation to the total body. Dempster's work allowed us, as well, to locate the centers of gravity of each of the body segments. From his work, we are capable of calculating how segmental masses and their locations influence the position of the total body center of gravity.

By applying Dempster's calculations to a body of known mass which is pictured on a film image, we can locate the total center of gravity of that body. We can then express that location as a percentage of the total body's standing height. This process comprises the cinematographical method of locating the body's center of gravity.

The balance board method for calculation of the body center of gravity is essentially the analysis of the forces applied to a second class lever system. The body lies upon a rigid board which comprises the lever in the system. The fulcrum to the system is placed under the board and directly beneath the body's feet. A weighing scale supports the opposite end of the balance board lever. The weight of the body provides the resistance to the system through the force of gravity and the weighing scale prevents the resistance from moving the lever. In this sense it can be considered the effort value in the lever system. By taking measurements on this system and performing the calculations of lever mechanics, the location of the theoretical center of gravity of the body supported by the lever can be accomplished. This location can also be expressed as a percentage of the standing height of the body.

A knowledge of the location of the total body center of gravity is of value to the analysis of body position and body motion. This theoretical point is the best single indicator of how the body is oriented within its environment or how from position to position the body is moved because it accounts for the position and motion of all the body's segments. If a general analysis of body motion is desired, a description of the motion of this theoretical point, the center of gravity, can provide that analysis.

EQUIPMENT

Slide of the human subject standing in the anatomical position
Slide projector
Graph paper
Balance board
Weighing scales
Measuring rule

REFERENCES

Dempster, W. "Space Requirements of the Seated Operator," **WADC Technical Report 55-158,** July, 1955, Wright Air Development Center, Air Research and Development Command, USAF, Wright-Patterson Air Force Base, Ohio.

Miller, D. I. and Nelson R. C. **Biomechanics of Sport.** Philadelphia: Lea and Febiger, 1973.

Wells, K. F. and Luttgens, K. **Kinesiology.** Philadelphia: W. B. Saunders Company, 1976.

PROCEDURES — Cinematographic Segmental Method

1. Using a slide projector, project the image of your subject onto the graph paper provided, making certain that the vertical line in the background of the slide matches a vertical line on the graph paper. Be certain, as well, that your subject's entire body image falls within the limits of the graph.

2. Trace the outline of your subject's body onto the graph paper using a sharpened pencil.

3. Place small, distinct dots on the graph paper to indicate each of the following anatomical landmarks or joint centers. These landmarks represent the boundaries of the body's segments.

   a. Vertex of the skull
   b. Sternal notch
   c. Midpoint between the hips
   d. Right and left shoulder joints
   e. Right and left elbow joints
   f. Right and left wrist joints
   g. Distal ends of the right and left third phalange of the hands
   h. Right and left hip joints
   i. Right and left knee joints
   j. Right and left ankle joints
   k. Distal ends of the right and left second phalange of the feet

4. Determine the rectangular coordinates for these segmental locations. Refer to the example below for assistance.

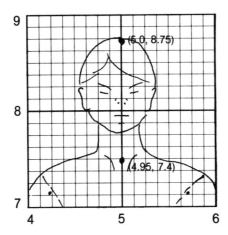

Distal Endpoint	−	Proximal Endpoint	×	Percentage Distance	+	Proximal Endpoint	=	Segmental Center of Gravity
1. Head and Neck								
X ((5.0	−	4.95)	×	.500)	+	4.95	=	4.975
Y ((8.75	−	7.4)	×	.500)	+	7.4	=	8.075

5. Transfer these coordinate values to their appropriate spaces on the sheet labeled Locations of Segmental Centers of Gravity.

6. Calculate the rectangular coordinates for each segmental center of gravity according to the formula presented below.

7. Transfer these segmental center of gravity coordinates to the Worksheet for Locating the Center of Gravity placing them into the appropriate spaces.

8. Multiply the X rectangular coordinate values times the presented segmental proportions of body weight. Repeat this procedure for each of the Y rectangular coordinates.

Body Segment	Proportion of Body Weight	X Value	X Product	Y Value	Y Product
1. Head and Neck	.079	4.975	0.393	8.075	0.638

9. Sum the columns of X and Y products to determine the rectangular coordinates of the total body center of gravity as it appears on your projected slide image.

10. Place a small star on this location of the body center of gravity on the graph paper.

11. Determine the average value for the Y coordinates of the distal ends of the right and left phalanges of the feet and use this average value as the floor position.

12. Subtract the floor position Y value from the Y value for the vertex of the skull to produce the relative body height.

13. Subtract the floor position from the Y value for the total body center of gravity to determine the center of gravity height.

14. Determine the percentage of standing height of the body center of gravity by dividing the Y value of the center of gravity height by the Y value of the relative body height.

PROCEDURES — Balance Board Method

1. Using the weighing scale, weigh your subject in the standing position. Record your subject's weight on your submission form.

2. Weigh the balance board as it is positioned horizontally on the scale. One end of the board will be on the scale and the other end of the board will be balanced off the floor on a fulcrum. Record the balance board weight on your submission form.

3. Assume a supine anatomical position on the balance board with your head towards the weighing scale and the plantar surfaces of your feet on line with the board's fulcrum. Record this weight (Loaded Balance Board Weight) on your submission form.

4. Measure the length of the balance board from the fulcrum line to the contact point on the scale. Record the balance board length on your submission form.

5. Calculate the theoretical weight of your body alone as it was positioned on the balance board. This requires subtracting the balance board weight from the loaded balance board weight.

6. Calculate the position of the total body center of gravity by applying the law of levers to your collected data:

$$\text{Center of Gravity Height} = (\text{Theoretical Body Weight} \times \text{Balance Board Length}) / \text{Total Body Weight}$$

7. Determine the percentage of standing height to the body center of gravity by dividing the center of gravity height (Proc. 6) by your total measured body height.

Diagram of Balance Board

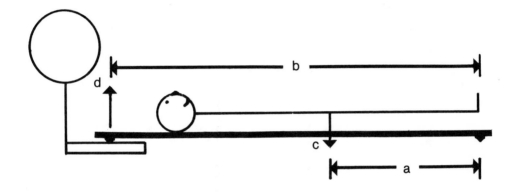

    a. Distance to body center of gravity
    b. Balance board length
    c. Total body weight
    d. Theoretical body weight

PROCEDURES — General

1. Verify the correctness of your hand computations as described by your laboratory instructor.

2. Draw comparisons between your calculated results and between your results and the supplied population norms to provide the basis for answers to the required questions.

SEGMENTAL ENDPOINTS NEEDED TO COMPUTE
THE TOTAL BODY CENTER OF GRAVITY

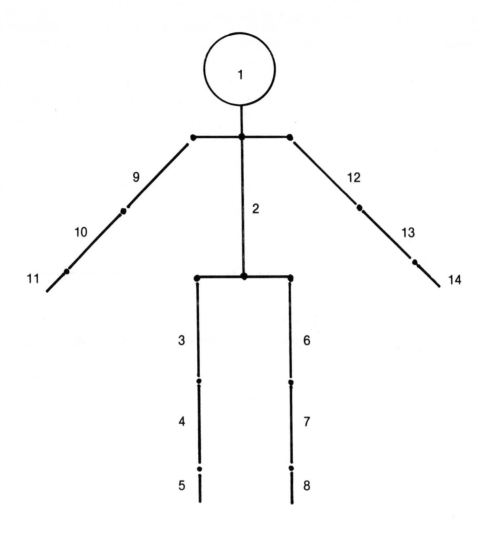

	Segment	Proximal Endpoint	Distal Endpoint
1.	Head and Neck	Mid Shoulders	Vertex of the Skull
2.	Trunk	Mid Hips	Mid Shoulders
3.	R. Thigh	R. Hip	R. Knee
4.	R. Leg	R. Knee	R. Ankle
5.	R. Foot	R. Ankle	R. Toe
6.	L. Thigh	L. Hip	L. Knee
7.	L. Leg	L. Knee	L. Ankle
8.	L. Foot	L. Ankle	L. Toe
9.	R. Upper Arm	R. Shoulder	R. Elbow
10.	R. Lower Arm	R. Elbow	R. Wrist
11.	R. Hand	R. Wrist	R. Finger Tip
12.	L. Upper Arm	L. Shoulder	L. Elbow
13.	L. Lower Arm	L. Elbow	L. Wrist
14.	L. Hand	L. Wrist	L. Finger Tip

SUBMISSION FORMS — Center of Gravity

Name _____ Section _____

Cinematographic Segmental Analysis

   Body Center of Gravity (Percentage of Height) = _____ . _____%

Direct Balance Board Method

   Body Center of Gravity (Percentage of Height) = _____ . _____%

QUESTIONS

Compare the two calculated percentages of body height for your total body center of gravity with the population norms presented in the laboratory introduction.

_____

_____

_____

_____

_____

_____

_____

_____

Speculate on any reasons for discrepancies between your calculated values and any discrepancies between those values and population norms.

_____

_____

_____

_____

_____

_____

_____

_____

_____

LOCATIONS OF SEGMENTAL CENTERS OF GRAVITY

1. Head and Neck

   X   ((_____ – _____) x .500) + _____ = _____

   Y   ((_____ – _____) x .500) + _____ = _____

2. Trunk

   X   ((_____ – _____) x .450) + _____ = _____

   Y   ((_____ – _____) x .450) + _____ = _____

3. R. Thigh

X   ((_____ − _____) x .433) + _____ = _____

Y   ((_____ − _____) x .433) + _____ = _____

4. R. Leg

X   ((_____ − _____) x .433) + _____ = _____

Y   ((_____ − _____) x .433) + _____ = _____

5. R. Foot

X   ((_____ − _____) x .429) + _____ = _____

Y   ((_____ − _____) x .429) + _____ = _____

6. L. Thigh

X   ((_____ − _____) x .433) + _____ = _____

Y   ((_____ − _____) x .433) + _____ = _____

7. L. Leg

X   ((_____ − _____) x .433) + _____ = _____

Y   ((_____ − _____) x .433) + _____ = _____

8. L. Foot

X   ((_____ − _____) x .429) + _____ = _____

Y   ((_____ − _____) x .429) + _____ = _____

9. R. Upper Arm

X   ((_____ − _____) x .436) + _____ = _____

Y   ((_____ − _____) x .436) + _____ = _____

10. R. Lower Arm

X   ((_____ − _____) x .430) + _____ = _____

Y   ((_____ − _____) x .430) + _____ = _____

11. R. Hand

X   ((_____ − _____) x .506) + _____ = _____

Y   ((_____ − _____) x .506) + _____ = _____

12. L. Upper Arm

X   ((_____ − _____) x .436) + _____ = _____

Y   ((_____ − _____) x .436) + _____ = _____

13. L. Lower Arm

X   ((_____ − _____) x .430) + _____ = _____

Y   ((_____ − _____) x .430) + _____ = _____

14. L. Hand

X   ((_____ − _____) x .506) + _____ = _____

Y   ((_____ − _____) x .506) + _____ = _____

WORKSHEET FOR LOCATING THE CENTER OF GRAVITY
USING THE SEGMENTAL METHOD

Body Segment	Proportion of Body Weight	X Value	X Product	Y Value	Y Product
1. Head and Neck	.079				
2. Trunk	.511				
3. R. Thigh	.097				
4. R. Leg	.045				
5. R. Foot	.014				
6. L. Thigh	.097				
7. L. Leg	.045				
8. L. Foot	.014				
9. R. Upper Arm	.027				
10. R. Lower Arm	.016				
11. R. Hand	.006				
12. L. Upper Arm	.027				
13. L. Lower Arm	.016				
14. L. Hand	.006				
Total Body Center of Gravity		X =		Y =	

Floor position = _____

Total body height = _____

Center of gravity height = _____

Percent of standing height to center of gravity = _____ . _____

WORKSHEET FOR LOCATING THE CENTER OF GRAVITY

USING THE BALANCE BOARD METHOD

Total Body Weight = _____ . _____ kgs.

Total Body Height = _____ . _____ cms.

Balance Board Weight = _____ . _____ kgs.

Balance Board Length = _____ . _____ cms.

Loaded Balance Board Weight = _____ . _____ kgs.

Theoretical Body Weight = _____ . _____ kgs.

$$\text{Theoretical Body Weight} = \text{Loaded Balance Board Weight} - \text{Balance Board Weight}$$

91

Body Center of Gravity Height = _____ . _____ cms.

Center of ＿ (Theoretical ✕ Balance / Total
Gravity Height ＝ Body Weight Board Length Body Weight

Center of Gravity's Percentage of Standing Height = _____ . _____%

Why do the norms suggest that the center of gravity is lower for women than men when each are in the anatomical position; give reasons for both men and women. _____

_____

_____

_____

_____

_____

_____

How does the position of the total body's center of gravity affect movement and performance, give an example using one specific activity? _____

_____

_____

_____

_____

_____

_____

_____

_____

_____

_____

_____

_____

_____

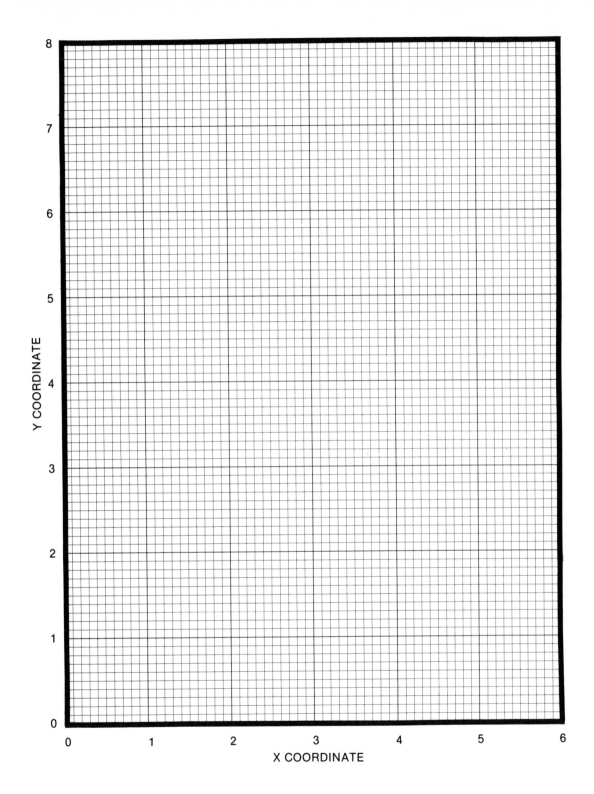

X COORDINATE

Y COORDINATE

TRANSFER OF MOMENTUM
and
EFFECTS OF EXTERNAL FORCES
on
PROJECTILE PATHS

PURPOSE

To evaluate the effect of momentum transfer upon the distance achieved in performing different styles of the standing long jump.

To evaluate the effects of action-reaction forces upon distances achieved in performing different styles of the standing long jump.

THEORY

The projectile path of the total body center of gravity is predetermined at the time of projection. Implicit to this statement is the assumption that only the external force of gravity will act upon the projectile once it has been projected. Other external forces would have some influence on this predetermined path.

Three factors serve to determine this projectile path: (1) the velocity at the time of projection, (2) the angle of projection, and (3) the height of projection if it differs from the landing height of the projectile. While this third factor is of some importance to activities such as shot put in which the height of projection and the height of landing are not the same, it is of little significance to the activity under consideration during this laboratory experience, the standing long jump. Here, only the first two factors will influence the projectile path. If we assume that each subject will perform the activity with a reasonable degree of consistency, that is, project his/her body at approximately the same angle each trial, then the primary factor which will influence the projectile path of the total body center of gravity will be its velocity at the time of projection. Alterations in this velocity factor will change the final measured distances of the jumps. One means for accomplishing this goal is through the transfer of momentum.

Transfer of momentum occurs when the rapid motion of one or more body parts is suddenly slowed to allow that momentum to pass to another body part. The most dramatic effects of this principle occurs when momentum is transferred from a larger body part to a smaller body part, but the transfer may occur in reverse. Observation of this principle, as it influences an activity, can be achieved by plotting velocity-time curves. If the velocity-time curves of adjacent body segments reveal that as the velocity of one segment decreases from its maximum as the velocity of the adjacent segment increases in velocity, then it is possible that momentum has been transferred efficiently from one segment to the other.

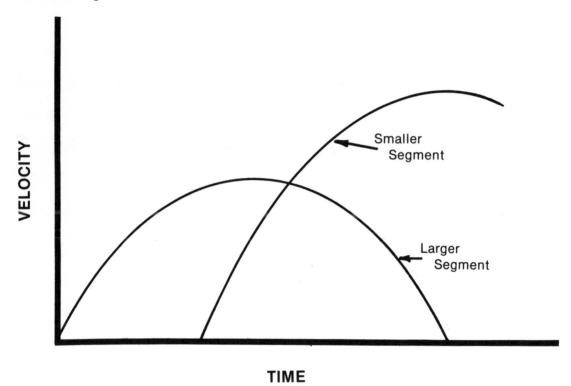

TIME

Momentum transfer is a factor common to many athletic activities. In throwing a ball, for instance, movement may be initiated by trunk rotation. The motion then flows successively down through the upper arm, the lower arm, and to the hand where final momentum is transferred to the ball. A velocity plot of this activity could reveal the existence of momentum transfer. Other common activities such as kicking a ball, striking a golf ball, and initiating most airborne activities in diving or trampolining all take advantage of this principle.

In ancient Olympic days, athletes performed the long jump while carrying weights in their hands. By manipulating these weights, they were able to achieve startling success according to present day standards. The athletes would swing the weights out in front of them as they projected themselves from the starting board. When the swing of these weights was stopped, momentum might have been transferred back to the body. At the peak of projection, the athletes would hurl the weights downward and backward providing an external action-reaction force intended to increase their velocity and hence project them further. In this single activity, these athletes attempted to take advantage of both transfer of momentum and action-reaction forces in a projectile motion.

EQUIPMENT

Measuring rules   ½ kg. weights   1 kg. weights

REFERENCES

Hay, J. G. **The Biomechanics of Sports, Techniques.** Englewood cliffs, New Jersey: Prentice-Hall, Inc., 1973, pp. 160-162.

Kelley, D. L. **Kinesiology: Fundamentals of Motion Description.** Englewood Cliffs, New Jersey: Prentice-Hall, Inc., 1971, pp. 135-140.

Wells, K. F. and Luttgens, K. **Kinesiology: Scientific Basis of Human Motion.** Philadelphia: W. B. Saunders Company, 1976.

HYPOTHESES

1. There will be no substantial differences among the mean standing long jump distances for the four different transfer of momentum techniques.

2. There will be no substantial difference between the two standing long jump mean distances with different action-reaction force magnitudes.

PROCEDURES

1. During all jumps, attempt to have your subject project his/her body at a 45 degree angle and with maximum velocity. This combination will produce maximum measured distance.

2. Perform three (3) standing long jumps using each of the following five (5) conditions: (NOTE: apply the five jumping conditions in a randomly selected order.)
   a. No arm swing (arms positioned one in front and one in back of the trunk)
   b. Normal arm swing
   c. Arm swing with ½ kg. weights in each hand (retain weights throughout the jump and landing)
   d. Arm swing with 1 kg. weights in each hand (retain weights throughout the jump and landing)
   e. Arm swing with ½ kg. weights in each hand (release the weights in a downward and backward direction while you are at the top of your flight path)

   NOTE: Condition e may require a number of practice trials prior to the three recorded trials.

3. Record the distance jumped (from jump line to rear of the nearest heel) and the total time in the air (from take-off to landing) on the submission forms.

4. Calculate the mean distance jumped, and the mean time in the air for each of the five jumping techniques and record each in the space provided.

5. Utilize the procedures described by your laboratory instructor to compute the required information to complete this laboratory experience.

6. From your computed information, record your results needed to test hypothesis number 1.

7. Indicate acceptance or rejection of hypothesis number 1, from your computed output determine the reason for your differences and report the implications of your findings.

8. From your computed information, record your results needed to test hypothesis number 2.

9. Indicate acceptance or rejection of hypothesis number 2, from your computed output determine the reason for your difference and report the implications of your findings.

SUBMISSION FORMS — Transfer of Momentum and External Effects on Projectiles

Name _____ Section _____

TRIAL CONDITION	TRIAL NO.	DISTANCE (CMS.)	TIME IN AIR (SECONDS)
a. No arm swing	1.	_____ . _____	_____ . _____
	2.	_____ . _____	_____ . _____
	3.	_____ . _____	_____ . _____
	Mean	_____ . _____	_____ . _____
b. Normal arm swing	1.	_____ . _____	_____ . _____
	2.	_____ . _____	_____ . _____
	3.	_____ . _____	_____ . _____
	Mean	_____ . _____	_____ . _____
c. ½ kg. weights retained	1.	_____ . _____	_____ . _____
	2.	_____ . _____	_____ . _____
	3.	_____ . _____	_____ . _____
	Mean	_____ . _____	_____ . _____
d. 1 kg. weights retained	1.	_____ . _____	_____ . _____
	2.	_____ . _____	_____ . _____
	3.	_____ . _____	_____ . _____
	Mean	_____ . _____	_____ . _____
e. ½ kg. weights released	1.	_____ . _____	_____ . _____
	2.	_____ . _____	_____ . _____
	3.	_____ . _____	_____ . _____
	Mean	_____ . _____	_____ . _____

NOTE: Attempt to release the weights downward and backward from the top of your jump. Practice will be required of the releasing trials prior to your performance.

DEFINITIONS

Transfer of Momentum _____
_____
_____
_____

Newton's Third Law of Motion _____

_____

_____

_____

Computed Jump Information

Condition A. (no arm swing)

Velocity

Horizontal (cm/sec) = _____

Vertical (cm/sec) = _____

Actual (cm/sec) = _____

Projection Angle (degrees) = _____

Impulse

Horizontal (kg-sec) = _____

Vertical (kg-sec) = _____

Condition B. (normal arm swing)

Velocity

Horizontal (cm/sec) = _____

Vertical (cm/sec) = _____

Actual (cm/sec) = _____

Projection Angle (degrees) = _____

Impulse

Horizontal (kg-sec) = _____

Vertical (kg-sec) = _____

Condition C. (½ kg. weight retained)

Velocity

Horizontal (cm/sec) = _____

Vertical (cm/sec) = _____

Actual (cm/sec) = _____

Projection Angle (degrees) = _____

Impulse

Horizontal (kg-sec) = _____

Vertical (kg-sec) = _____

Condition D. (1 kg. weight retained)

Velocity

Horizontal (cm/sec) = _____

Vertical (cm/sec) = _____

Actual (cm/sec) = _____

Projection Angle (degrees) = _____

Impulse

Horizontal (kg-sec) = _____

Vertical (kg-sec) = _____

Condition E. (½ kg. weight released)

Velocity

Horizontal (cm/sec) = _____

Vertical (cm/sec) = _____

Actual (cm/sec) = _____

Projection Angle (degrees) = _____

Impulse

Horizontal (kg-sec) = _____

Vertical (kg-sec) = _____

Test of Hypothesis #1

Condition	Mean Distance (cm.)
A. (no arm swing)	_____
B. (normal arm swing)	_____
C. (½ kg. weight retained)	_____
D. (1 kg. weight retained)	_____

Hypothesis #1 was found to be (circle)   TRUE   FALSE

Reasons for differences (if any) _____

_____

_____

_____

Implications of your findings _____

_____

_____

_____

Test of Hypothesis #2

Condition   Mean Distance (cm.)

C. (½ kg. weight retained)   _____

E. (½ kg. weight released)   _____

Hypothesis #2 was found to be (circle)   TRUE   FALSE

Reasons for differences (if any) _____

_____

_____

_____

Implications of your finding _____

_____

_____

_____

If printed computer output is used during this laboratory report, be sure to attach the computer printout to these submission forms at the time you submit them.

Why should the use of weights enhance the distance of the standing long jump? _____

_____

_____

_____

_____

_____

Explain a reason why the computed angles of projection for your subject were lower or higher than the optimum 45° desired angle. _____

_____

_____

_____

_____

_____

WORK AND POWER
verification of
sargent jump test

PURPOSE

To perform calculations of mechanical work, power, and component force output based upon easily obtained measures of displacement and time.

To determine the relationships between commonly accepted measures of power and previously calculated measures of power.

THEORY

Mechanical work is accomplished when a force is applied against a resistance, succeeds in overcoming the inertia of that resistance, and causes it to move some measure of distance. Mechanical work is evaluated as the product of this force output and the distance the resistance is moved:

MECHANICAL WORK = FORCE X DISTANCE RESISTANCE IS MOVED

The quantity of mechanical work effected will depend upon the situation in which the work is attempted. If an object weighing 10 kgs. is lifted vertically 10 m., then 100 kg-meters of mechanical work has been accomplished. However, a different quantity of force would be required in order to push that resistance 10 m. along a horizontal surface and so a different quantity of mechanical work would be performed. In this case, the forces needed to overcome the effects of friction would need to be accounted for and evaluated throughout the distance the resistance was moved.

Work is therefore a vector quantity possessing the characteristics of both magnitude and direction. If work is attempted at some angle other than the vertical or horizontal, actual work accomplished will be the sum of these vector components.

Mechanical and physiological work is not synonymous. While mechanical work always requires a resistance to be moved some distance, physiological work does not. In an isometric muscular contraction, for instance, energy is expended as force is applied against a resistance but the magnitude of that force is not sufficient to cause the resistance to move. Physiological work has been accomplished, but mechanical work has not. Motion, then, is a prerequisite to the existance of mechanical work.

Power is the representation of the rate at which mechanical work is accomplished:

POWER = MECHANICAL WORK / TIME REQUIRED FOR THAT WORK

From this definition, power depends not only on the quantity of mechanical work accomplished, but also on the time needed to accomplish it. As this work increases or as the time decreases, power will increase.

Horsepower is the conventional representation of power output:

1 HORSEPOWER = 76.25 KG - METERS PER SECOND

Muscular power tests have been consistently included in general motor ability and motor fitness batteries. These tests have had a long history not without criticism. Many tests, and variations upon these tests, have been proposed and used to examine the muscular power of the legs. Most common among these tests have been the techniques of vertical jumping and most prevalent among the vertical jumps has been the Sargent Vertical Jump. The frequency with which new tests of leg power arise as well as the number of modifications which are then imposed upon these tests and the amount of research devoted to the issue reveals the debate about the dilemma of discovering a test to measure pure leg power. Despite the realization that pure power moves are not encountered in athletics, the need to measure muscular power as an indication of performance or as a reference for personal abilities remains.

This laboratory experience will examine several variations on the Sargent Vertical Jump test and seek relationships between these tests of power and another test of power capable of simple measurement and calculation. While the appropriateness of these tests to physical fitness batteries or as indicators of personal characteristics may be at issue, the mechanical factors involved are not insignificant if observed in the frame-work within which they are generated.

EQUIPMENT

Vertical jump board
Chalk
Stairway
Timing devices
Measuring rule or tape

REFERENCES

Clark, H. H. "Muscular Power of the Legs", **Physical Fitness Research Digest,** Series 8, No. 2, President's Council on Physical Fitness and Sports, April, 1978.

Sargent, D. A. "The Physical Test of a Man", **American Physical Education Review,** 26, No. 4, p. 188, April, 1921.

Sullivan, W. J. and Considine, W. J. "Relationship of Selected Tests of Leg Strength and Leg Power on College Men", **Research Quarterly,** 44:404, December, 1973.

PROCEDURES — Direct Calculation of Mechanical Work and Power

1. Measure your subject's body weight.

2. Select a flight of stairs containing at least nine stairs.

3. Measure the vertical lift of the stairs from stair 3 to stair 9 and record this value on your submission form.

4. Place the timing devices available so the time taken to climb from stair 3 to stair 9 may be determined.

5. Your subject is to begin his/her trial 6 meters from the bottom stair and is to run up the stairs as rapidly as safely possible, taking 3 steps at a time.

6. The time to traverse from stair 3 to stair 9 should be taken during each of three performances and recorded in the spaces provided on the submission forms.

7. Power may then be determined for each trial by applying the following formula:
POWER = (Body Weight (KGS.) x Vertical Lift) / Elapsed Time

PROCEDURES — Vertical Jump Measurements

1. Perform three standing vertical jumps while jumping from both legs and record each jump's height on the submission form in the space provided. Indicate the maximum value for the jumps under this condition.

2. Perform three standing vertical jumps while jumping from your dominant leg and record each jump's height on the submission form in the space provided. Indicate the maximum value for the jumps under this condition.

3. Perform three standing vertical jumps while jumping from your non-dominant leg and record each jump's height on the submission form in the space provided. Indicate the maximum value for the jumps under this condition.
NOTE: All jumps are to be conducted without prior steps, the subject is to assume a stationary position at the base of the board and perform all jumps with two or less complete arm swings.

PROCEDURES — Statistical

1. Submit your maximum calculated power value, and the heights of your three vertical jumps to your laboratory instructor, so that determinations of appropriate correlations can be made.

2. After accumulation of all subject scores, correlations among the variables will be provided to you and should be recorded in the appropriate space on your submission forms.
NOTE: In using correlations to make predictions of other values, the higher the correlation, the more accurate the prediction.

SUBMISSION FORMS — Work and Power

Name _____ Section _____

Direct Calculation of Mechanical Work and Power

    Subject Weight _____ kgs.

    Vertical lift of stairs from stair 3 to stair 9 _____ meters

    Time from stair 3 to stair 9

        Trial 1 _____ sec.

        Trial 2 _____ sec.

        Trial 3 _____ sec.

    Calculated Power

        Trial 1 _____ kg-meters/sec.

        Trial 2 _____ kg-meters/sec.

        Trial 3 _____ kg-meters/sec.

        Maximum calculated power _____ kg-meters/sec.

Vertical Jump Height - both legs

    Heights

        Trial 1 _____ cms.

        Trial 2 _____ cms.

        Trial 3 _____ cms.

        Maximum measured height _____ cms.

Vertical Jump Heights - dominant leg

    Heights

        Trial 1 _____ cms.

        Trial 2 _____ cms.

        Trial 3 _____ cms.

        Maximum measured height _____ cms.

Vertical Jump Heights - non-dominant leg

    Heights

        Trial 1 _____ cms.

        Trial 2 _____ cms.

        Trial 3 _____ cms.

        Maximum measured height _____ cms.

Statistical Test Results

    Correlation (both leg jump score vs. power) _____ . _____

Correlation (dominant leg jump score vs. power) _____ . _____

Correlation (non-dominant leg jump score vs. power) _____ . _____

QUESTIONS

For your laboratory group, which of the three vertical jump tests best predicted power?

_____

Why would you speculate that this was so? _____

_____

_____

Name a sport performance where leg power as evaluated by this test would be an advantage. _____

Why would leg power be an advantage? _____

_____

_____

How would you help one of your performers in this activity to gain the leg power which is needed? (be specific) _____

_____

_____

_____

_____

VELOCITY
analysis of the
baton exchange

PURPOSE

To determine a quantitative value for the velocity of performance of runners and utilize this information to more efficiently perform the relay baton exchange in track.

THEORY

In order to completely describe and understand the performance of an athlete in an event where time is a criteria of measure, it is necessary for the physical educator to examine the rates at which performances occur. Two terms have been applied to the rate of performance, these are speed and velocity. Because the term speed is a scalar quantity and does not, in its measure, indicate a direction, utilization of this measure eliminates a portion of the possible description and is very difficult to obtain through calculation procedures. Therefore, during this laboratory experience, we will be concerned with only the quantity "velocity" which because of its vector properties allows description by both magnitude and direction.

As an impulse (net-force applied for a time period) is applied to an object, the observable result is the change in velocity of the object. This concept appears to be one of the most important concepts in all of sport. The contrary is also true, no change in velocity over a time period indicates no net-force has been applied. It is therefore obvious that, if no net-force is applied to an object moving at optimum velocity a very efficient activity is being performed.

Because it is the purpose of the relay events in track to move a baton through the prescribed distance in the most efficient manner, this objective can best be achieved by allowing the baton to continue to travel at a constant rate throughout the race. Based on quantitative observations, the baton appears to vary velocity most during the exchange phases of the event. To explain this occurrence, it is necessary to describe the baton exchange. The exchange occurs as the incoming runner passes the baton to the outgoing runner. As the incoming runner reaches some position prior to the exchange zone, the outgoing runner begins running from a stationary position with the expectation that at the time he/she achieves the same velocity as the incoming runner, they will be in a position so that an efficient baton exchange can be made.

It is therefore the objective of this laboratory experience to have you predict the time when the outgoing runner should start so that the optimum baton exchange can be made. This will be accomplished by determining velocity — time curves of the incoming and outgoing runners and through determination of the intersection of these curves, indicate and demonstrate how an efficient exchange can be predicted.

EQUIPMENT

5 start syncronized clocks
Planimeter

PROCEDURES

1. At the end of each of five equal intervals throughout the described relay exchange zone, position timers whose responsibility will be to stop the syncronized clocks as a runner passes immediately in front of their station.

2. Allow the selected incoming runner to run one leg of the relay with the completion of that distance at the end of the exchange zone. While the runner passes through this zone, the timers should stop the syncronized clocks as described above. Record the results of this timing procedure in the appropriate locations on the submission forms.

3. Subtract each subsequent time from the previous time to produce the time required for the subject to pass through each of the equal displacement intervals. Record each of these times on the submission forms under the column marked "adjusted time."

4. Compute the incoming runner's average velocity for each of the intervals by dividing the displacement in that interval by the time necessary to traverse that interval (adjusted time for that interval), and record these velocities in the spaces provided on the submission forms.

5. Compute the mean velocity of the incoming runner by adding the 5 previously recorded average velocities and dividing by 5. Record this value in the appropriate space on your submission form.

6. Plot this mean velocity as a straight dotted line across the Velocity-Time graph provided.

7. Allow the selected outgoing runner to start at the beginning of the exchange zone. While the runner accelerates through the exchange zone, the timers should stop the syncronized clocks as described in procedure 1. Record the results of this timing procedure in the appropriate locations on your submission form.

8. Subtract each subsequent time from the previous time to produce the time required for the subject to pass through each of the equal displacement intervals. Record each of these times on the submission form under the column marked "adjusted time."

9. Compute the outgoing runner's average velocity for each of the intervals by dividing the displacement in that interval by the time necessary to traverse that interval (adjusted time for that interval), and record these velocities in the spaces provided on the submission form.

10. Using the original recorded time, determine the time for each interval which most

110

closely approximates the time midpoint of that interval, and record these in the spaces provided in the column "Mean Interval Time" on your submission form.

11. Plot each coordinate pair (Mean Interval Time, Velocity) as a dot on the same graph that was previously used for the mean velocity of the incoming runner.

12. Connect the outgoing runner's coordinate dots by a smoothly curving solid line.

13. Indicate the spot where the incoming runner's velocity-time curve crosses the outgoing runner's velocity-time curve with a small star.

14. With the assistance of your instructor and through the use of the provided scale value, use the planimeter to determine the difference in displacement between the incoming and outgoing runners during the exchange, as illustrated by the shaded area in the figure below. Area A.

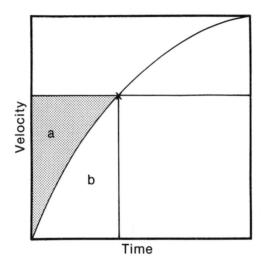

15. Position the outgoing runner at the beginning of the exchange zone and a start marker behind the outgoing runner at the calculated difference in displacement between the two runners.

16. Allow the incoming runner to again run his/her leg of the relay. Have the outgoing runner assume his/her starting position at the beginning of the exchange zone. When the incoming runner reaches the start marker, tell the outgoing runner to start. The two runners should reach equal velocities at some point in the exchange zone and at that point the exchange should occur.
NOTE: Area B in the above figure represents the displacement from the beginning of the exchange zone to the position of the actual exchange.

SUBMISSION FORMS — Velocity

Name _____ Section_____

Incoming Runner

Station	Time	Adjusted Time	Velocity
0	0		
1	_____sec.	_____sec.	_____meters/sec.
2	_____sec.	_____sec.	_____meters/sec.
3	_____sec.	_____sec.	_____meters/sec.
4	_____sec.	_____sec.	_____meters/sec.
5	_____sec.	_____sec.	_____meters/sec.

Mean incoming runner's velocity _____meters/sec.

Outgoing Runner

Station	Time	Adjusted Time	Velocity
0	0		
1	_____sec.	_____sec.	_____meters/sec.
2	_____sec.	_____sec.	_____meters/sec.
3	_____sec.	_____sec.	_____meters/sec.
4	_____sec.	_____sec.	_____meters/sec.
5	_____sec.	_____sec.	_____meters/sec.

Stations	Mean Interval Times
0-1	_____sec.
1-2	_____sec.
2-3	_____sec.
3-4	_____sec.
4-5	_____sec.

What difficulties were encountered during attempting to make this prediction?

_____
_____
_____
_____
_____
_____

Did the baton exchange occur during your trial run? _____

Were the runners too fast, too slow, or correctly times? _____

How could you correct for the errors you may have made in your prediction?

_____

_____

_____

_____

_____

_____

How could you utilize this technique in track coaching of various performers?

_____

_____

_____

_____

_____

_____

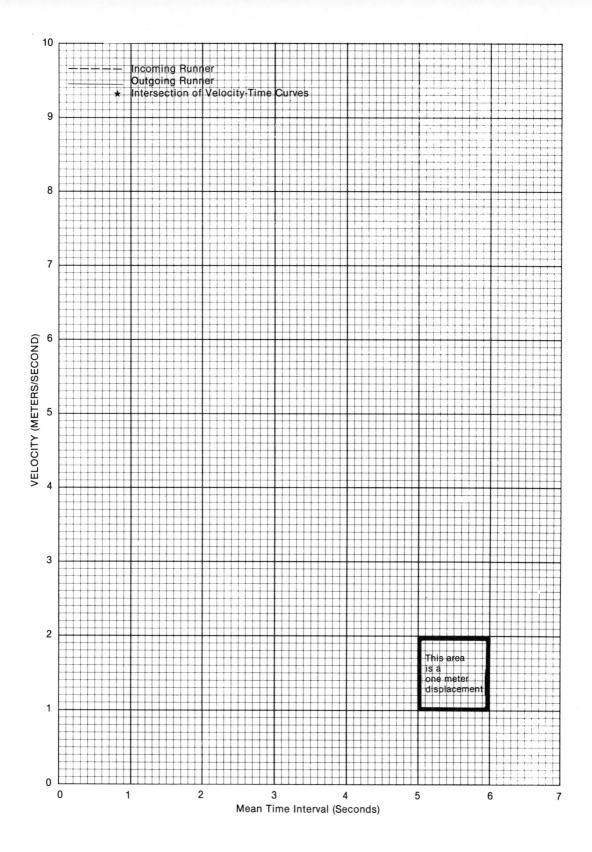

LESSON PLAN

PURPOSE

To allow you to structure a lesson based on your knowledge of a skill and its related mechanical principles.

To expose you to a teaching situation.

To allow for a review of information related to mechanical principles, near the end of your instruction in this material.

THEORY

The utilization of information provides for another learning exposure as well as a chance to more completely understand concepts based on mechanical principles presented as lecture material.

The preparation of your lesson plan will allow you to select those principles which you feel are important to the performance of your selected skill.

The observation of your classmates' teaching will allow for your questions and evaluation of teaching methods, as well as observation of other applications of similar mechanical principles.

REFERENCES

Hay, J. G. **The Biomechanics of Sports Techniques,** Englewood Cliffs, New Jersey: Prentice-Hall, Inc., 1973.

Kelly, D. L. **Kinesiology: Fundamentals of Motion Description,** Englewood Cliffs, New Jersey: Prentice-Hall, Inc., 1971.

Wells, K. F. and Luttgens, K. **Kinesiology: Scientific Basis of Human Motion,** Philadelphia: W. B. Saunders Co., 1976.

PROCEDURES

1. Select a sport skill you would like to teach.

2. Create a lesson plan for a selected grade level, and on this plan describe the sequence and method to be used in teaching the selected skill.

3. On the lesson plan forms, provide:

    a. All the information at the top of the form including grade level you are teaching.

    b. A sequential list of those portions of the skill to be taught in the order in which you will teach them.

    c. For each portion of the skill listed, provide a verbal description of the pointers you will use to assist in your presentation of this information.

    d. Present a list of those mechanical principles which you think are being presented as you teach each portion of the skill.

NOTE: your lesson plan will be collected by your laboratory instructor at the beginning of your lab period. If you need your lesson plan to teach from, make a copy before comming to lab.

NOTE: You will be grouped so that all persons teaching similar skills will present and demonstrate prior to the discussion of any member of that skill group.

4. Present your lesson to your classmates (approx. 5 min.), assuming they are in the grade to which your lesson is directed. (Be prepared to answer questions.)

5. While observing other presentations, evaluate these by listing sequentially those mechanical principles you thought were covered. A comparison will be drawn between teaching evaluations and lesson plans to determine if the lesson was presented successfully.

SUBMISSION FORM   Name _____   Section _____

Skill Being Taught _____   Grade Level _____

Portion of Skill Being Taught	Pointers Given	Mechanical Principles
1.		
2.		
3.		
4.		
5.		
6.		
7.		
8.		
9.		

SUBMISSION FORM (continued)   Name _____

Portion of Skill Being Taught	Pointers Given	Mechanical Principles
10.		
11.		
12.		

Teaching Evaluation

Skill _____

Teacher _____

Mechanical Principles (in order)

Name _____

Teaching Evaluation

Skill _____

Teacher _____

Mechanical Principles (in order)

Name _____

Teaching Evaluation

Skill _____

Teacher _____

Mechanical Principles (in order)

Name _____

Teaching Evaluation

Skill _____

Teacher _____

Mechanical Principles (in order)

Name _____

Teaching Evaluation

Skill _____

Teacher _____

Mechanical Principles (in order)

Name _____

Teaching Evaluation

Skill _____

Teacher _____

Mechanical Principles (in order)

Name _____

Teaching Evaluation

Skill _____

Teacher _____

Mechanical Principles (in order)

Name _____

Teaching Evaluation

Skill _____

Teacher _____

Mechanical Principles (in order)

Name _____

Teaching Evaluation

Skill _____

Teacher _____

Mechanical Principles (in order)

Name _____

- - - - - - - - - - - - - - - - - - - -

Teaching Evaluation

Skill _____

Teacher _____

Mechanical Principles (in order)

Name _____

Teaching Evaluation

Skill _____

Teacher _____

Mechanical Principles (in order)

Name _____

Teaching Evaluation

Skill _____

Teacher _____

Mechanical Principles (in order)

Name _____

Teaching Evaluation

Skill _____

Teacher _____

Mechanical Principles (in order)

Name _____

Teaching Evaluation

Skill _____

Teacher _____

Mechanical Principles (in order)

Name _____

Teaching Evaluation

Skill _____

Teacher _____

Mechanical Principles (in order)

Name _____

Teaching Evaluation

Skill _____

Teacher _____

Mechanical Principles (in order)

Name _____

Teaching Evaluation

Skill _____

Teacher _____

Mechanical Principles (in order)

Name _____

Teaching Evaluation

Skill _____

Teacher _____

Mechanical Principles (in order)

Name _____

Teaching Evaluation

Skill _____

Teacher _____

Mechanical Principles (in order)

Name _____

Teaching Evaluation

Skill _____

Teacher _____

Mechanical Principles (in order)

Name _____

QUANTITATIVE MOTION ANALYSIS

PURPOSE

To perform a quantitative analysis of a selected sport or locomotive skill.

To compare your quantitative findings with your expectations and speculate on why any differences may exist.

THEORY

Cinematography (motion pictures) and video recordings are used extensively to retain images which represent human performance in sport or human locomotor skills. The recorded representative images may be viewed in sequence to reproduce the motion as it occurred or be stopped and viewed separately to allow for subjective scrutinization. Advancing frame by frame through the recorded images gives the trained observer, not only an indication of the body motions, but also the relative times at which each body part is moved.

Subjective evaluation of motion by the described method has proven acceptable in gross evaluation but provides no method for exact measurements or comparisons of results. With these needs in mind, a quantitative method of analysis was designed. This method requires the evaluation of a number of recorded images each of which occurred in a particular time sequence and all of which were recorded from the same position.

The quantitative method for analysis described in the following procedures may be applied to any movement which can be assumed to be uniplanar (occur in one plane) and which can be recorded by one of the methods listed above.

The most extensively evaluated measurement used in quantitative human motion analysis is the action of the total body's center of gravity. This theoretical point, about which all the body's mass is centered, is moved by motions of any or all of the body parts and best represents the motions of the total body. Because of the frequent use of this point in biomechanical literature to describe body motion, the analysis to be performed in this laboratory experience will also center around the computed movements of this very descriptive point.

EQUIPMENT

Sequential slide sets of human performances (or) cinematographic recording of human performance (based on availability at your facility).

131

Appropriate projectors

Optional — computer program for total body center of gravity computation

REFERENCES

Dempster, W. "Space Requirements of the Seated Operator," **WADC Technical Report 55-158,** Wright Air Development Center, Air Research and Development Command, USAF, Wright-Patterson Air Base, Ohio, July, 1955.

Miller, D. I. and Nelson, R. C. **Biomechanics of Sport,** Philadelphia: Lea and Febiger, 1973, pp. 18-21.

Cooper, J. M., Adrian, M. and Glassow, R. B. **Kinesiology,** St. Louis: C. V. Mosby Co., 1982.

PROCEDURES

1. Obtain a set of sequential slides or cinematographic recordings from your laboratory instructor. Each set of slides or recordings will be provided with a reference sheet indicating the following information:
   a. The frame rate of the cinematographic recording.
   b. The actual length of the length reference measure.
   c. The numbers of the frames which are presented in the sequence (including why these frames were selected).

2. Align the projector provided so that its optical axis is perpendicular to the plane on which the image is to be projected. Be sure that the projector to screen distance provides that the entire field of vision of the slide will be presented on the graph papers provided.

3. Project the length reference slide onto one of the graph papers provided. Be sure that the image is in sharp focus, and that the vertical and/or horizontal reference position(s) fall along a vertical and/or horizontal line(s) on the graph paper.

4. Using the spaces provided on Submission Form 1, determine the conversion factor for linear measures by following these procedures:
   a. On the graph paper, mark the ends of the length reference measure with small but distinct dots.
   b. Determine the rectangular coordinates of each of the end dot positions, recording them in the spaces provided on your submission form.
   c. Record the actual length of the reference measure in the space provided.
   d. Determine the projected length of the reference measure using the application of the Pythagorean Theorm presented.
   e. Determine the length conversion factor by dividing the actual length by the projected length of the reference measure.

   NOTE: This number represents the number of real life units which appears on each unit of the graph paper.

5. Using the graph pages provided, for each of the supplied frames conduct the following procedures to produce measurable stick figure body representations:
   a. Project the selected image onto the graph paper. Be sure that the stationary reference points from this and all previous or subsequent images are located at exactly the same rectangular coordinate positions and that the vertical and/or horizontal reference position(s) fall along vertical and/or horizontal lines(s) of the graph paper.
   b. Focus the film carefully. Do not change projector's position once you have begun these procedures.

c. Using a sharpened pencil, locate small but distinct dots on your graph paper to represent the locations of the following 19 segmental endpoints:

a. Vertex of the skull
b. Midpoint between the shoulders
c. Midpoint between the hips
d. Right and left shoulder joints
e. Right and left elbow joints
f. Right and left wrist joints
g. Distal ends of the right and left third phalange of the hands
h. Right and left hip joints
i. Right and left knee joints
j. Right and left ankle joints
k. Distal ends of the right and left second phalange of the feet

NOTE: If a segmental endpoint is hidden, an estimate of its location must be made and a dot must be placed at that location.

d. Once all 19 segmental endpoints have been located or estimated, draw lines to connect those endpoints which form the body's 14 segments. The endpoints to be connected and the segment formed are listed below:

Segment	Proximal	Distal
Head and Neck	Mid Shoulders	Vertex of the Skull
Trunk	Mid Hips	Mid Shoulders
R. Thigh	R. Hip	R. Knee
R. Leg	R. Knee	R. Ankle
R. Foot	R. Ankle	R. Toe
L. Thigh	L. Hip	L. Knee
L. Leg	L. Knee	L. Ankle
L. Foot	L. Ankle	L. Toe
R. Upper Arm	R. Shoulder	R. Elbow
R. Lower Arm	R. Elbow	R. Wrist
R. Hand	R. Wrist	R. Finger Tip
L. Upper Arm	L. Shoulder	L. Elbow
L. Lower Arm	L. Elbow	L. Wrist
L. Hand	L. Wrist	L. Finger Tip

e. For the 19 segmental endpoints, describe next to each its rectangular coordinates in the format (X,Y), these points will be used for total body center of gravity location.
f. Repeat this procedure for each of the frames required to completely describe the activity.

6. From the data reduced during the previous procedures, quantitative measurements describing the motion which occurred may be made. Some of these measurements may be more applicable to some motions than others. Your laboratory instructor should assist you in your selection and specific application of these measurements.

a. Total body center of gravity location — this measure is applicable to describing most activities because it is the best indication of the position of the total body and provides a bases for the description of the body's motion without regard for its individual parts. In most cases your laboratory instructor will describe the procedures for computer utilization in assisting with these computations. If no computer is available, copies of the work sheets from the "Center of Gravity" laboratory experience may be made and used for this procedure.
b. Total body center of gravity path — on one of the sheets of graph paper provided,

plot the rectangular coordinate positions of each of the subsequent center of gravity locations. Connect these points with a smoothly flowing curve to represent the path traversed during the motion of the total body.

c. Joint angular measures — measurement of a joint angle in subsequent frames indicates quantitatively the motion occurring at that joint. This may be done through the use of extended segmental lines and protractor measurement or through an application of trigonometric functions. Your laboratory instructor will assist you in selecting the joint most appropriate for analysis during your activity, and will direct you as to the technique for obtaining your measurements.

d. Joint angular change — for the selected joint, plot a graph which represents the angular changes which occurred in that joint during the time of the performance. On the graph paper provided, plot coordinate points of angle on the ordinate (vertical) and time on the abscissa (horizontal), for each of the frames provided by your instructor. Connect the points plotted by a smoothly curving line which indicates your estimate of the motions occurring at that joint during the movement.

7. Based on the measurements previously made to determine the center of gravity position at various times during the activity (procedure 6 (a)), interesting and informative graphics may be produced. Velocity-time graphs are probably the most informative graphic presentation which can be made in a biomechanical kinematic analysis. Through simple interpretation, information such as velocity at a point in time, displacement between points in time, or acceleration at a time may be determined. Since the motion analyzed is assumed to exist in only one plane, only motions which have occurred in the vertical or the horizontal directions may be described during the analysis process. With this in mind and to assist with future descriptions, velocity-time curves for both the vertical and horizontal motions need to be produced.

a. Vertical Velocities and Vertical Velocity-Time Graph

1. Using the format on Submission Form 2, record the vertical positions (Y coordinates), of the total body center of gravity in the spaces provided for each of the frames analyzed. Adjacent to each vertical position, record the time at which that position occurred.

2. Determine the vertical displacement between every two adjacent positions by subtracting the previous positions' Y coordinate from the subsequent positions' Y coordinate for each pair of positions. Record each calculated vertical displacement in the appropriate Scale Vertical Displacement space provided on Submission Form 2.

3. Using the information computed in Procedure 4, multiply the length conversion factor (real life units per graph paper unit) times each of the calculated Scale Vertical Displacements to produce an associated Actual Vertical Displacement. The units for this value will be meters.

4. Determine the time interval encompassed between every two adjacent positions by subtracting the previous position's associated time from the subsequent position's associated time for each pair of positions. Record each calculated time interval in the appropriate Time Interval space provided on Submission Form 2.

5. Determine the mean time which exists between every two adjacent positions by adding the previous position's associated time to the subsequent position's associated time and dividing the sum produced by two (2). Record each calculated mean time in the appropriate Mean Time space provided on Submission Form 2.

6. Determine the average vertical velocity between every two adjacent positions

by dividing each Actual Vertical Displacement by its associated Time Interval (NOTE: not the mean time between those positions.) Record each calculated Vertical Velocity in the appropriate Vertical Velocity space provided on Submission Form 2.

7. On the graph paper provided, plot a vertical velocity-time curve by drawing a small point to represent each of the calculated vertical velocities as measured on the ordinate (vertical) and its associated mean time as measured on the abscisca (horizontal). Connect the points plotted by a smoothly curving line which represents the changing vertical velocity of your performer's center of gravity during the activity. This graph will be utilized to assist you in the required evaluation of the motion.

b. Horizontal Velocities and Horizontal Velocity-Time Graph

Repeating the procedures previously outlined for vertical measures in Procedure 7, section a, parts (1) through (7) using horizontal measures and Submission Form 3 will produce similar required information and graphic presentations needed for evaluation of horizontal motions. NOTE: Time values associated with each position or displacement interval (Time, Time Interval, and Mean Time) are the same for each frame number regardless if the measures are vertical or horizontal.

8. Using the information previously accumulated, perform the following evaluations on the numeric data calculated or on data presented in graphic form. NOTE: Not all general evaluations may be equatably important to all activities.

a. In the spaces provided on your submission forms, answer the questions provided based on your data.

b. On your center of gravity path plot, place a circle on the graph at the position which you estimate to be the beginning of the action phase of the motion, and a star on the graph to represent the end of the action phase. (The Action Phase for a motion is that phase needed in the development of force.)

c. On the graph of your selected joint action, indicate the points in time which represent the beginning and ending of the action phase of the movement with dotted vertical lines.

d. On the graph of the horizontal and vertical velocities, indicate the points in time which represent the beginning and ending of the action phase of the movement with dotted vertical lines.

e. On each of the velocity-time graphs, draw a sloping line which is tangent to the curve at that point in time which represents the end of the action phase of the movement. Estimate a numeric value for that slope by dividing the rise by the run for the line. (For each 1 graph paper unit horizontal (run), what is the rise or fall in the vertical direction?)

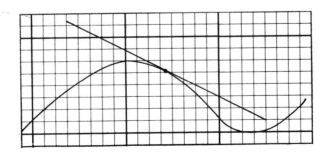

f. On each of the velocity-time graphs, estimate the area encompassed by the curve presented from the beginning to the end of the action phase. This area may be

135

measured by use of a planimeter or the encompassed unit boxes may be counted by hand.

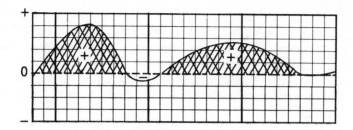

The areas above the abscissa are valued as positive, those below this line are valued as negative. The algebraic sum of positive and negative traversals represents the area encompassed.

SUBMISSION FORMS — Quantitative Motion Analysis

Name _____   Section _____

Submission Form 1 — Length Conversion Factor

   Length Conversion Factor Coordinates

      Right End   X = _____   Y = _____

      Left End   X = _____   Y = _____

   Actual Reference Measure Length = _____meters

   Projected Length Calculation

    X(length) = X(right end) − X(left end)

    _____ = _____ − _____

    Y(length) = Y(right end)-Y(left end)

    _____ = _____ − _____

    Projected length = $\sqrt{(X(length))^2 + (Y(length))^2}$

    _____ = $\sqrt{(\rule{2cm}{0.4pt})^2 + (\rule{2cm}{0.4pt})^2}$

   Conversion Factor Calculation

    Conversion factor = Actual length / Projected length

    _____ = _____/_____

Submission Form 2 — Vertical Velocities

Frame No.	Vertical Position (units)	Time (sec.)	Scale Vertical Displacement (units)	Actual Vertical Displacement (meters)	Time Interval (sec.)	Mean Time (sec.)	Vertical Velocity (meters/sec.)
1.							
2.							
3.							
4.							
5.							
6.							
7.							
8.							
9.							
10.							

Submission Form 3 — Horizontal Velocities

Frame No.	Horizontal Position (units)	Time (sec.)	Scale Horizontal Displacement (units)	Actual Horizontal Displacement (meters)	Time Interval (sec.)	Mean Time (sec.)	Horizontal Velocity (meters/sec.)
1.							
2.							
3.							
4.							
5.							
6.							
7.							
8.							
9.							
10.							

Submission Form 4 — Evaluation of Analysis

1. Describe the calculated path of total body center of gravity in relation to the associated body movements which occurred during the activity.

_____

_____

_____

_____

_____

_____

_____

2. Describe verbally, the motion of the body's center of gravity during the action phase of the performance. Based on the objectives of the performance, is this motion what you would have expected? Why?

_____

_____

_____

_____

_____

_____

_____

_____

3. Did the selected joint move from flexion to extension or hyperextension, or from extension or hyperextension to flexion during the action phase of the motion? Describe the muscle(s) or muscular group(s) you would expect to be active, their type of contraction, their direction of contraction, and their ballisticity of contraction based on the information presented on the "joint action graph."

Kinesiological terminology for joint motion during the action phase

_____

Muscular groups you would expect to be active _____

_____

Why? _____

_____

_____

_____

140

Type of muscular contraction for these groups _____

Why? _____

_____

_____

_____

_____

Direction of the muscular contraction for those groups _____

Why? _____

_____

_____

_____

_____

Ballisticity of muscular contraction for those groups _____

Why? _____

_____

_____

_____

_____

4. Describe how the vertical velocity changed for the performer during the action phase. Were these changes what you would have expected prior to beginning your evaluation? Why?

_____

_____

_____

_____

_____

_____

_____

5. Describe how the horizontal velocity changed for the performer during the action phase. Were these changes what you would have expected prior to beginning your evaluation? Why?

_____

_____

_____

_____

_____

_____

_____

_____

6. The slope of the velocity-time curve at any point in time indicates the acceleration which is occurring to the body's center of gravity at that time.

A. Vertical Acceleration

1. Describe the vertical acceleration occurring to the body's center of gravity at the end of the action phase for the motion. Speculate on a possible cause for this acceleration.
   (NOTE: $F = ma$)

   _____

   _____

   _____

   _____

2. What effect is this acceleration having on the vertical velocity of the body's center of gravity at that time?

   _____

   _____

   _____

   _____

3. Is the change or lack of change in the vertical velocity of the body's center of gravity what you would have expected prior to beginning your evaluation? Why?

   _____

   _____

   _____

   _____

B. Horizontal Acceleration

1. Describe the horizontal acceleration occurring to the body's center of gravity at the end of the action phase for the motion. Speculate on a possible cause for this acceleration.
   (NOTE: $F = ma$)

   _____

   _____

_____

_____

2. What effect is this acceleration having on the horizontal velocity of the body's center of gravity at that time?

_____

_____

_____

_____

3. Is the change or lack of change in the horizontal velocity of the body's center of gravity what you would have expected prior to beginning your evaluation? Why?

_____

_____

_____

_____

7. The area encompassed by a velocity-time curve between any two points in time represents the displacement of the body's center of gravity during that time period.

A. Vertical Displacement

1. What is the quantity of vertical displacement of the body's center of gravity during the action phase of the movement?

_____

_____

2. Is the vertical displacement of the body's center of gravity during the action phase of the movement what you would have expected prior to the beginning of your evaluation? Why?

_____

_____

_____

_____

B. Horizontal Displacement

1. What is the quantity of horizontal displacement of the body's center of gravity during the action phase of the movement?

_____

_____

_____

2. Is the horizontal displacement of the body's center of gravity during the action phase of the movement what you would have expected prior to the beginning of your evaluation? Why?

_____

_____

_____

_____

8. Describe the one feature of your quantitative motion analysis which produced the most unexpected results. Why was this particular feature unexpected? Speculate on the reason for the occurrance of this feature.

_____

_____

_____

_____

_____

_____

_____

_____

_____

_____

_____

_____

_____

_____

_____

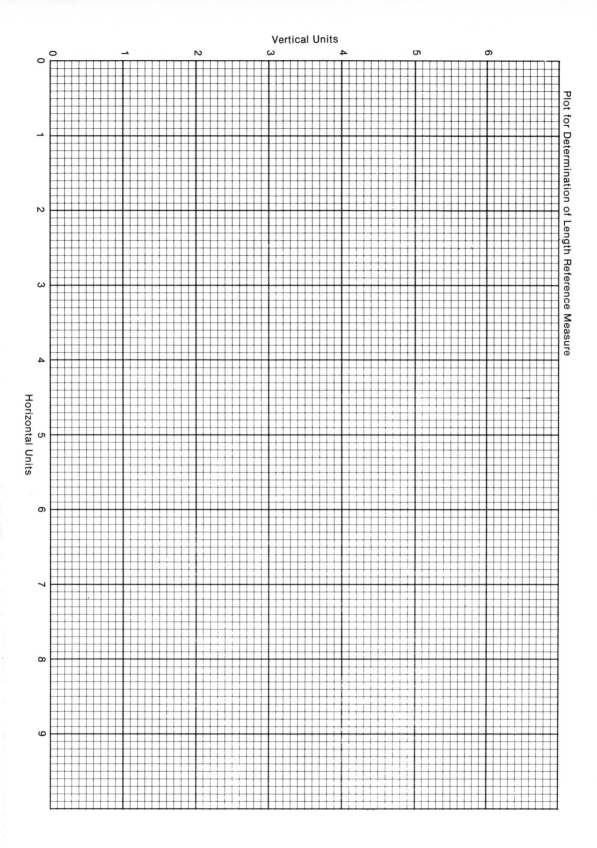

Vertical Units

Horizontal Units

Plot for Determination of Length Reference Measure

145

Vertical Units

Horizontal Units

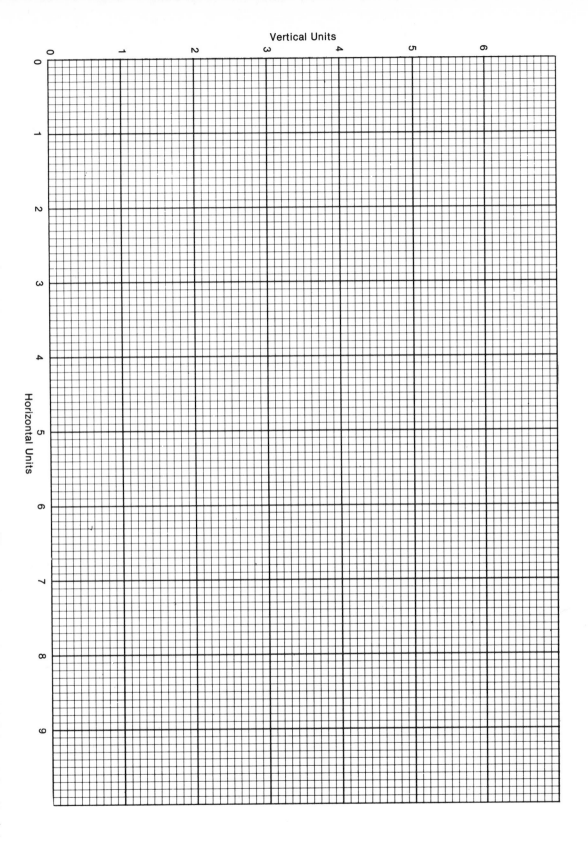

147

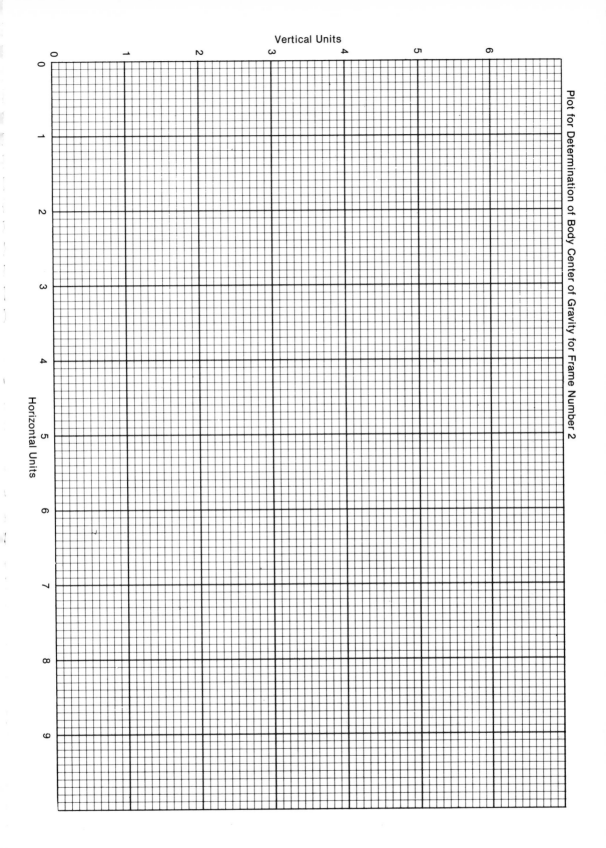

Plot for Determination of Body Center of Gravity for Frame Number 2

Vertical Units

Horizontal Units

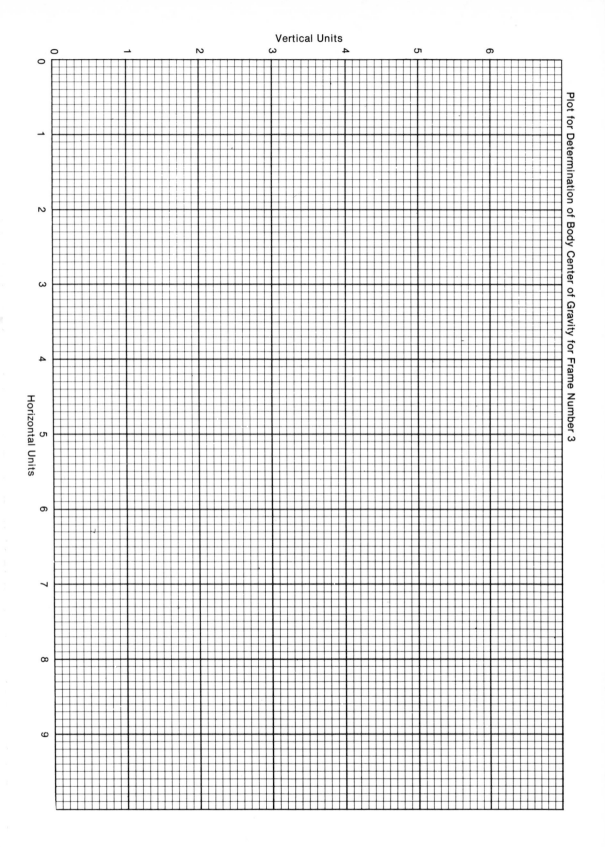

Vertical Units

Horizontal Units

Plot for Determination of Body Center of Gravity for Frame Number 3

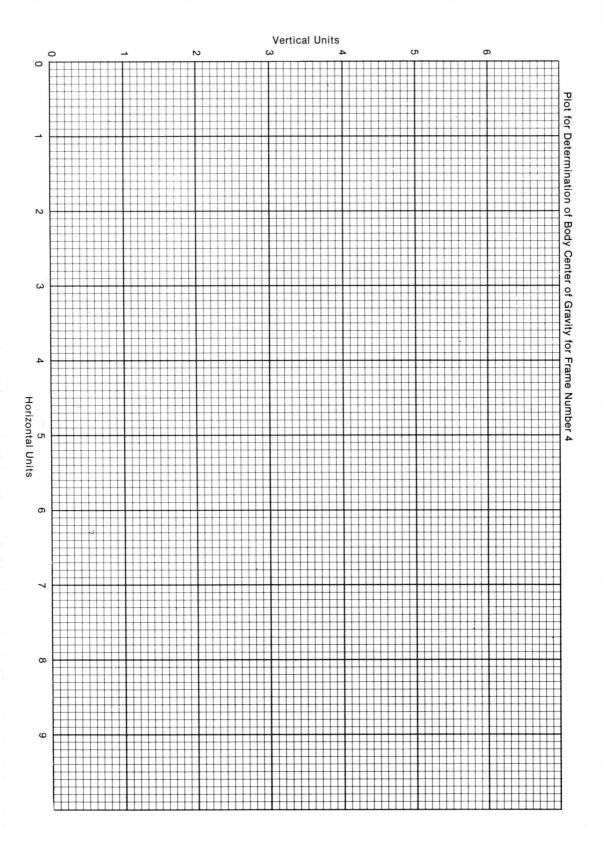

Vertical Units

Horizontal Units

Plot for Determination of Body Center of Gravity for Frame Number 4

153

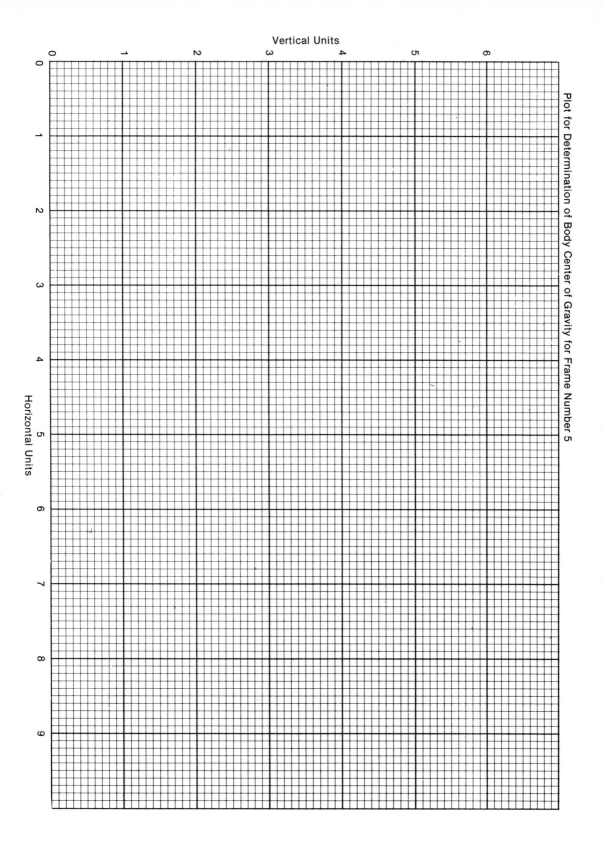

Vertical Units

Horizontal Units

Plot for Determination of Body Center of Gravity for Frame Number 5

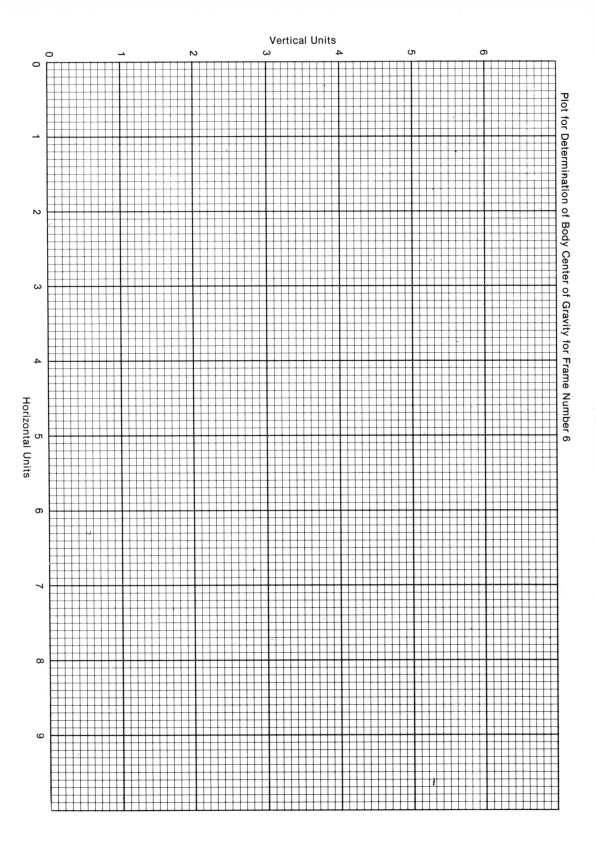

Vertical Units

Horizontal Units

Plot for Determination of Body Center of Gravity for Frame Number 6

Vertical Units

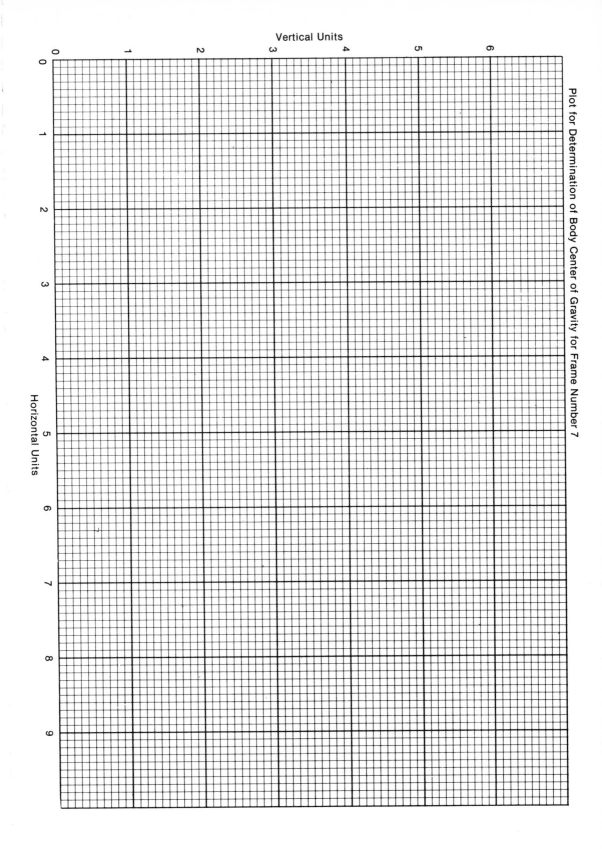

Plot for Determination of Body Center of Gravity for Frame Number 7

Horizontal Units

Vertical Units

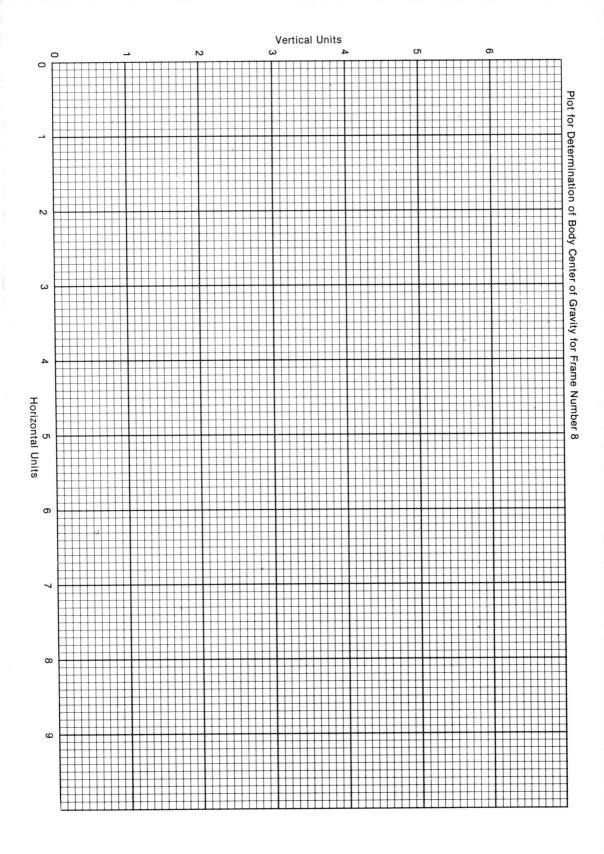

Horizontal Units

Plot for Determination of Body Center of Gravity for Frame Number 8

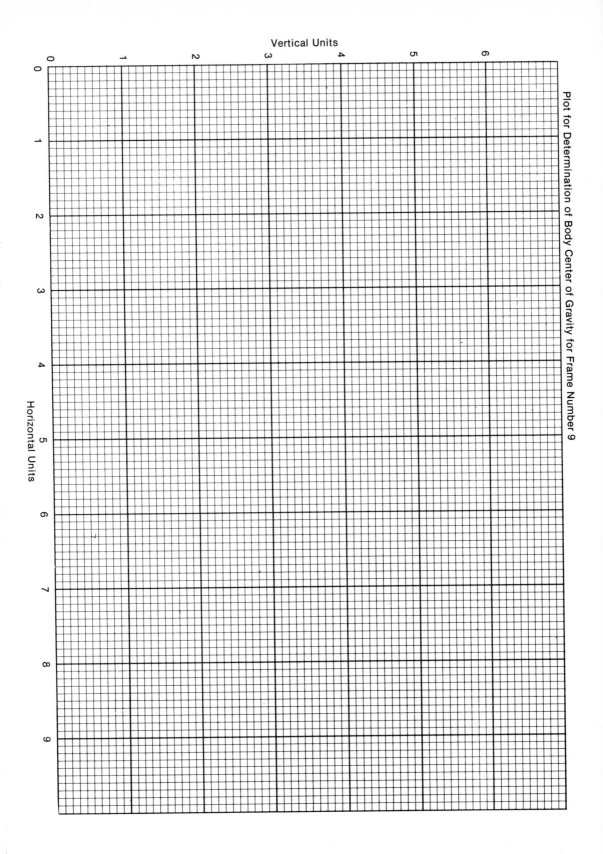

Plot for Determination of Body Center of Gravity for Frame Number 9

Vertical Units

Horizontal Units

163

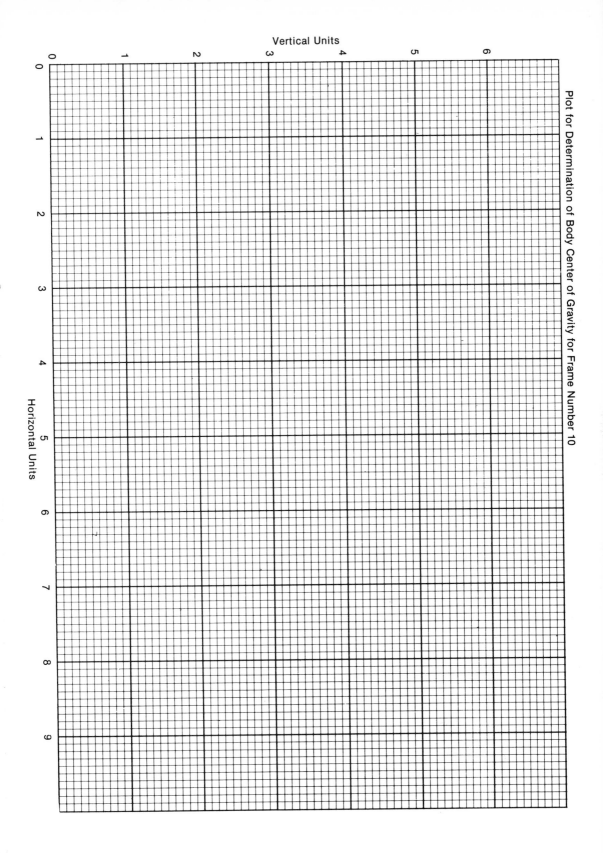

Plot for Determination of Body Center of Gravity for Frame Number 10

Vertical Units

Horizontal Units

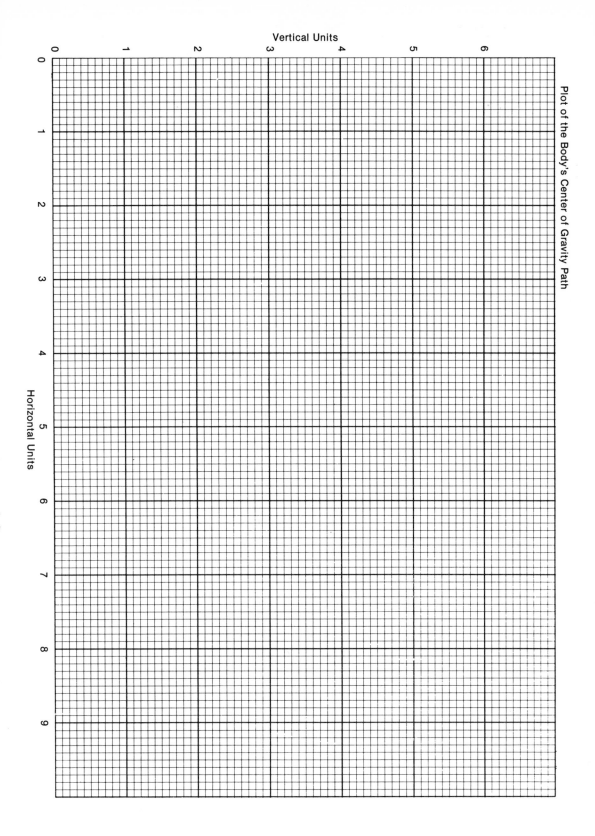

Vertical Units

Horizontal Units

Plot of the Body's Center of Gravity Path

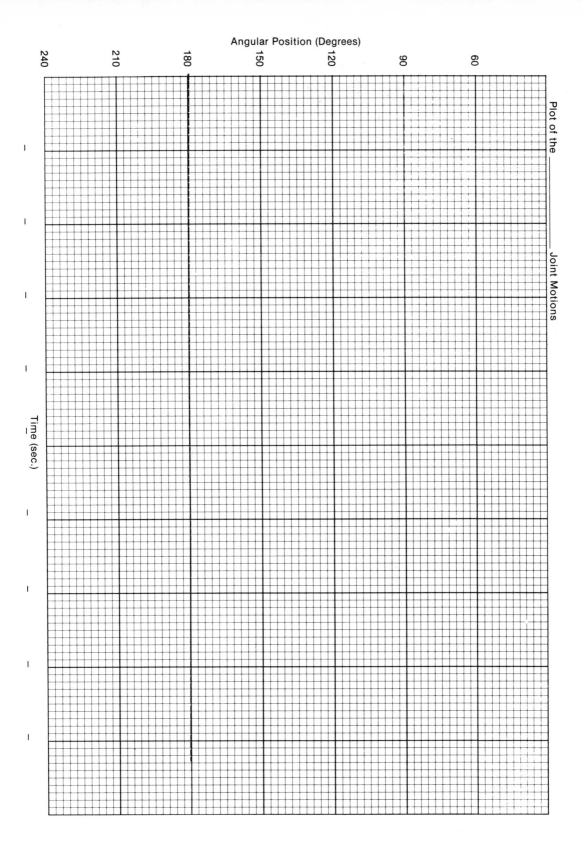

Angular Position (Degrees)

Plot of the _____ Joint Motions

Time (sec.)

169

Vertical Velocity (meters/sec.) +

0   +   +   I+

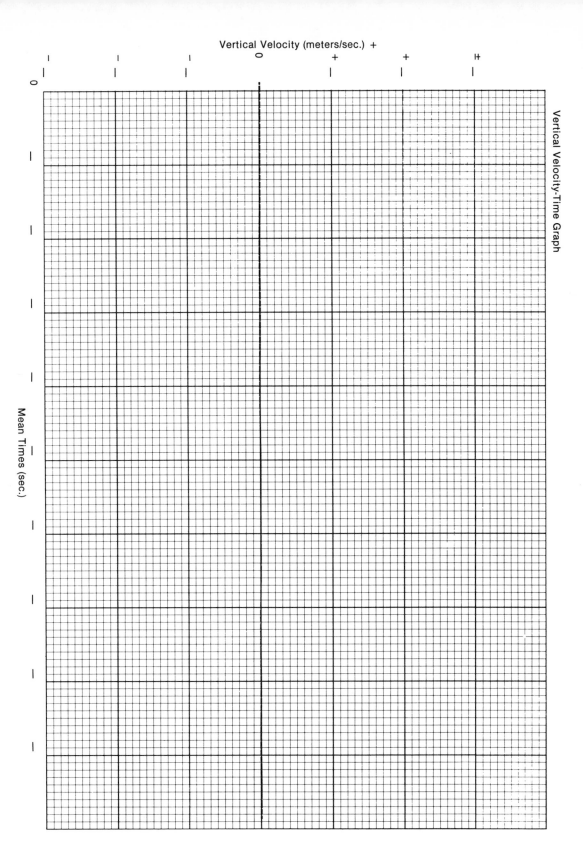

Vertical Velocity-Time Graph

Mean Times (sec.)

Horizontal Velocity (meters/sec.) +

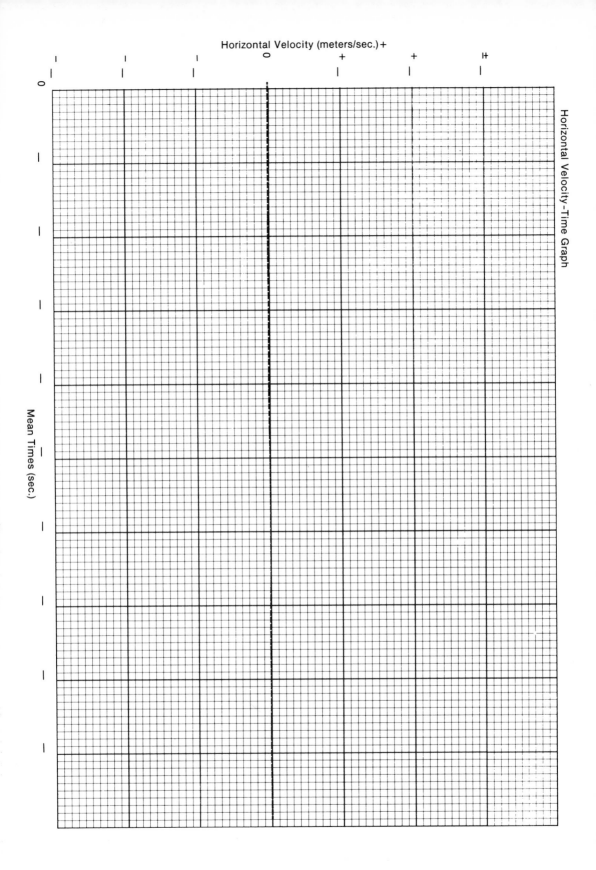

Horizontal Velocity-Time Graph

Mean Times (sec.)